THE EDGE OF SPACE

The
EDGE
of
SPACE

Exploring the upper atmosphere

Richard A. Craig

Illustrations by Joyce A. Lake

1968
DOUBLEDAY & COMPANY, INC.
GARDEN CITY, NEW YORK

RICHARD A. CRAIG was born in Abington, Massachusetts, in 1922. He received the A.B. degree cum laude from Harvard University in 1942 and served in the Air Force from 1942 to 1946. During this period he received meteorology training as an Aviation Cadet at the Massachusetts Institute of Technology, and was assigned as a weather forecaster, then to research duties at M.I.T. and later at the Woods Hole Oceanographic Institution. While at M.I.T., he earned the M.S. degree in meteorology. After leaving the Air Force, he worked for a few months at Woods Hole, and then returned to M.I.T. where he received the Sc.D. in meteorology in 1948. He was employed by the Harvard College Observatory as a Research Fellow from 1948 to 1951 and then joined the Air Force Cambridge Research Center as a Branch Chief and Research Meteorologist. In 1958, Dr. Craig joined the faculty of the Florida State University as a Professor and has remained there to date.

Dr. Craig has served the American Meteorological Society in various capacities and is currently Chairman of the Society's Committee on the Mesosphere and Thermosphere. He is a Fellow of the Society.

Library
UNIVERSITY OF MIAMI

Library of Congress Catalog Card Number 68–10568
Copyright © 1968 by Educational Services Incorporated
All Rights Reserved
Printed in the United States of America
First Edition

THE SCIENCE STUDY SERIES

This book is one of a number that will appear in the series through the collaboration of Educational Services Incorporated and the American Meteorological Society.

The Science Study Series was begun, in 1959, as a part of the Physical Science Study Committee's program to create a new physics course for American high schools. The committee started its work in 1956, at the Massachusetts Institute of Technology but subsequently became the nucleus of Educational Services Incorporated, of Watertown, Massachusetts, which has carried on the development of new curricula in several fields of education, both in the United States and abroad. The work in physics has had financial support from the National Science Foundation, the Ford Foundation, the Fund for the Advancement of Education, and the Alfred P. Sloan Foundation.

The purpose of the series is to provide up-to-date, understandable, and authoritative reading in science for secondary school students and the lay public. The list of published and projected volumes covers many aspects of science and technology and also includes history and biography.

The series is guided by a Board of Editors: Bruce F. Kingsbury, Managing Editor; John H. Durston, General Editor; Paul F. Brandwein, of the Conservation Foundation and Harcourt, Brace & World, Inc.; Samuel A. Goudsmit, Brookhaven National Laboratory; Philippe LeCorbeiller, Harvard University; and Gerard Piel, *Scientific American.*

Selected Topics in the Atmospheric Sciences

The American Meteorological Society, with the objectives of disseminating knowledge of meteorology and advancing professional ideals, has sponsored a number of educational programs designed to stimulate interest in the atmospheric sciences. One such program, supported by the National Science Foundation, involves the development of a series of monographs for secondary school students and laymen, and since the intended audiences and the standards of excellence were similar, arrangements were made to include their volumes on meteorology in the Science Study Series.

This series within a series is guided by a Board of Editors consisting of James M. Austin, Massachusetts Institute of Technology; Richard A. Craig, Florida State University; James G. Edinger, University of California, Los Angeles; and Verne N. Rockcastle, Cornell University. The society solicits manuscripts on various topics in the atmospheric sciences by distinguished scientists and educators.

PREFACE

I wrote this monograph because I wanted to communicate to the young potential scientist and to the mature and interested non-scientist some of the excitement of the rapidly developing studies of the earth's upper atmosphere. The objective implies an intelligent audience, but one with limited technical background. It is not easy to write about complex subjects for such an audience. On the one hand one must not assume prior knowledge of certain facts and concepts; on the other hand, one must avoid oversimplification and a condescending attitude. There is a fine line between the two that should be followed, and I ask the reader's indulgence and understanding if I have not always followed it exactly.

I should like to acknowledge the substantial help of my son, Malcolm A. Craig. He went over the original manuscript carefully and suggested many changes that I believe have made the material more understandable and interesting. I am also indebted to the editors and reviewers of the American Meteorological Society, of Educational Services, Inc., and of Doubleday & Company, Inc., for many valuable suggestions.

CONTENTS

I

Introduction

On October 4, 1957, an astonished world learned that Soviet scientists had succeeded in putting man's first artificial satellite into orbit. During the ensuing weeks, millions watched the night sky in the hope of getting a glimpse of the "Sputnik" and wondered at its significance and meaning. Many people judged this significance entirely in the light of international politics and the balance of military power. Others saw that it was a giant step toward the eventual exploration of space and of other planets. Only a few realized that it was a logical continuation of man's scientific exploration of the upper atmosphere, an exploration that had been going on for more than half a century, but in a form that usually had not attracted widespread public attention.

Nevertheless, the earlier exploration of the upper atmosphere was an absolutely necessary prelude to the launching of artificial satellites. Engineers had to know how high above the earth Sputnik must be in order that it would not be so slowed down by the atmosphere that it would plunge immediately back to earth. It was imperative to know the physical environment in which satellites would travel, especially the later manned capsules. What is solar radiation like at such altitudes? How many meteors approach the atmosphere from above? What is the composition of the atmosphere at great altitude? What is the temperature? To what extent is the atmosphere ionized? Observations from satellites have helped to answer these questions, but, in fact, partial answers were available before satellites were used.

The many ingenious methods that scientists have used to gather this information and what they have learned about the upper atmosphere will be the subject of this book.

Troposphere and Stratosphere

At the turn of the century, man had already learned much about the air near the earth's surface. He also knew something about the upper air. For instance, from a few kite and balloon measurements he learned that the air temperature decreases as one goes upward and away from the surface. Although these measurements reached up to less than 10 km (6.2 miles), it was generally supposed that the temperature must fall indefinitely with increasing altitude to a value of absolute zero (−459°F or −273°C) at the "edge of space." In fact, some scientists were ready with explanations of why this had to be so.

All this was changed by the careful measurements of a patient French scientist, Léon Philippe Teisserenc de Bort, who in April of 1902, after years of work, finally felt justified in refuting the theory that the temperature continually decreases with increasing altitude. He based his tradition-shattering conclusions on the results of 236 separate balloon flights (a tremendous number of observations for that time), all of which had reached an altitude of 11 km or more. Teisserenc de Bort had also tried his hand at observations from kites, but with less success. On one occasion, eleven of his kites escaped and floated across Paris, trailing miles of wire. They stopped a steamboat and a train, and cut off telegraph communication with Rennes, on the day that the results of the famous Dreyfus court-martial in that city were being anxiously awaited.

Teisserenc de Bort's many balloon observations above the 10-km level were not consistent with the theory of the time. He had found that, beginning somewhere between 8 and 12 km above the earth's surface, the temperature stopped decreasing. In fact, his measurements showed that there might even be a slight increase. As the large number of his observations attests, Teisserenc was at first very wary of these revolutionary results and thought he should blame his instruments. Because of his uncertainty it was years before he was confident enough to announce his conclusions before the French academy. Within a month, the German scientist Dr. Richard Assman announced that he had independently arrived at the same conclusion. However, he based his results on only five balloon flights—a far cry from the caution of his French colleague. Teisserenc de Bort's work emphasizes the importance of meticulous observations in advancing man's scientific knowledge.

Teisserenc's discovery is closely related to our definition of the "upper atmosphere." We will take the upper atmosphere to mean all of the atmosphere above that level where the temperature stops decreasing. This varies with latitude but averages about 10 km. The atmosphere below this point is known as the *troposphere*. As a matter of fact, this term was suggested by Teisserenc himself in 1908. He derived it from the Greek word *tropein*, meaning to "turn over," because the troposphere is a region of convection, with rising and sinking currents of air. For the air above the troposphere, he first suggested the term "isothermal layer" and later the name *stratosphere*. This name he derived from the Latin word *stratum*, meaning "a flat layer," because of the absence of convection.

The word stratosphere is now generally taken to mean the layer of air extending from about 10 km to about 50 km, at which level the temperature reaches a maximum value. Above the stratosphere are two more layers: the *mesosphere* extends above the stratosphere to about 80 km, and the *thermosphere* is the name given to the atmosphere above 80 km. Figure 1 shows this system of nomenclature, along with the change in average temperature with increasing altitude.

This definition of the upper atmosphere is far from universal. Some scientists consider that the "upper atmosphere" begins at a higher level, in some cases as high as 80 km. However, for many purposes it is logical to separate the troposphere from the rest of the atmosphere. The tropopause, which is the dividing line between the troposphere and the stratosphere, varies in altitude depending upon the latitude at which it is being measured and, to a much lesser extent, on the time of the year. The altitude of the tropopause varies from an average of about 6 km at the poles to about 18 km above the equator. It is higher in the warmer months than during the cold season, and seasonal variation is most pronounced in the middle latitudes.

The troposphere is the layer of air in which we have our "weather," or, as Teisserenc said, the region where

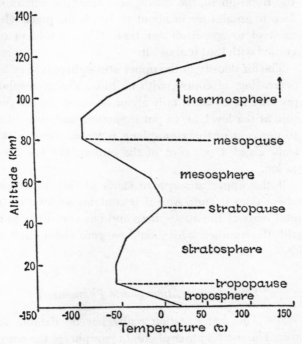

Figure 1. Atmospheric Nomenclature and Temperature
      Change

the air "turns over." Nearly all clouds are found in the troposphere, and rain, snow, sleet, and hail all fall from these clouds. All our violent storms—hurricanes, tornadoes, thunderstorms, and cyclones—are born in this lower atmosphere or "weather-sphere." Most air travel does not leave the troposphere, with the exception of U-2's and other high-flying jets, satellites, and the new supersonic transports being developed by the United States, Great Britain, France, and the Soviet Union to carry passengers in the stratosphere. Thus,

the troposphere, the atmosphere from the earth's surface to an altitude of about 10 km, is the place where
most of us spend all our time. We are seldom concerned with the air above it.

The air density in the upper atmosphere is very low,
decreasing, of course, with altitude. The atmospheric
pressure at 16 km is only about one-tenth of the pressure at sea level, or, to put it another way, only about
10 per cent of the atmosphere is found above 16 km.
Only about 1 per cent of the atmosphere lies above
30 km.

If the upper atmosphere starts at the tropopause,
where does it end? And if it contains so little of the
total mass of the atmosphere and has very little to do
with the weather, why should we care about studying
it?

Some Upper Atmospheric Phenomena

The first question really has no definite answer. The earth's atmosphere, to paraphrase the words
made famous by General MacArthur, never really
stops, it just fades away. The air density and pressure
decrease gradually, and the atmosphere gradually
merges with interplanetary space, which itself still has
some molecules. Exactly where one wishes to say that
the atmosphere ends and space begins is quite arbi-
trary and depends a good deal on what phenomenon
one is interested in. The reader can make his own
choice as he learns about these phenomena.

The second question, "Why should we study the upper atmosphere?", has many answers. One of these has
already been mentioned: the upper atmosphere is the
environment of satellites and a stairway to space ex-

ploration. Some other answers will be mentioned here and covered more thoroughly later in this book.

As a starter, interestingly enough, without the upper atmosphere we would all be dead. Ozone (O_3), the triatomic form of oxygen, which is found mostly above the troposphere, absorbs certain lethal ultraviolet[1] radiation from the sun. Ironically, ozone itself is poisonous; but only a negligible quantity is found in the lower atmosphere. Even where the concentration of ozone (the density of ozone divided by the density of air) is greatest (at about 30 km), there are only about 10 molecules of O_3 for every million molecules of normal oxygen (O_2) and nitrogen (N_2). Despite its relative scarcity, ozone has an important effect on the temperature of the atmosphere. In fact, as we will discuss later, it is the reason for the temperature rise in the upper part of the stratosphere (see Figure 1). In addition, because ozone is poisonous to humans, as well as corrosive to some materials such as rubber, the new supersonic transports for passenger flights in the stratosphere must be designed with this in mind.

Most people have, at one time or another, seen a "shooting star." However, the object that flashes across the heavens and leaves a bright trail of light that is visible for a second or two is not a "star" at all. It is a tiny particle of metallic "dust" called a meteor, which probably will burn up before reaching the tropo-

[1] Ultraviolet radiation is radiation with a wavelength too short to be seen by the human eye. Visible light ranges from a wavelength of about 4000 A to about 7000 A. Light of less than 4000 A wavelength is in the ultraviolet, and light of greater than 7000 A wavelength is in the infrared. "A" stands for a very small unit of length, called the Angstrom. There are 100,-000,000 Angstroms in 1 centimeter. See also Chapter 4 and Table 1.

sphere. The upper atmosphere shields us from this shower of meteors which is constantly bombarding the earth. Only an insignificantly small number of the largest meteors penetrates the troposphere to reach the earth's surface. When they do they are called meteorites. Some minute particles, known as micrometeorites, also escape vaporization and settle to the earth as dust. We shall see in Chapter 2 and Chapter 7 that studies of meteors have told us much about the upper atmosphere.

The ionosphere,[2] which is that part of the earth's atmosphere where there are enough ions and free electrons to affect radio waves, begins at a level in the vicinity of 50 to 70 km above the earth. These ions and electrons reflect radio waves back to earth where they may be picked up by radio receivers at long distances from the transmitting site. Otherwise, ordinary commercial radio communication over distances of more than about 100 km would be impossible, because of the curvature of the earth. The low parts of the ionosphere (D and E regions) reflect the longest waves, and shorter wavelengths are reflected from a higher region, called the F region. The effect of such phenomena as sunspots (which are discussed in detail in Chapter 4) on the ionosphere therefore also has an effect on radio transmission. Figure 2 shows the reflection of radio waves from these ionospheric layers. Radar and television signals are not reflected by the ionosphere because their wavelengths are too short.

[2] In the ionosphere, some of the air molecules and atoms are ionized, that is, sunlight has caused them to lose one or more of their electrons. Thus, in this region there are some ions (atoms or molecules with one or more electrons missing) and some free electrons. The ionosphere will be discussed more fully in Chapter 6.

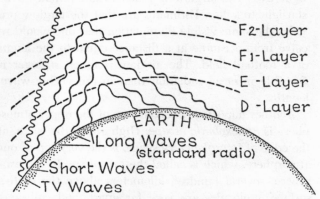

Figure 2. Reflection of Radio Waves from the Ionosphere

The *aurora borealis* and the *aurora australis*, those spectacularly colored displays of light which sometimes shine down from the night sky, are interesting phenomena in themselves. Anyone who has seen the "Northern lights" or the "Southern lights" will agree. It is significant that the aurorae, which are the result of material particles bombarding our atmosphere from the sun, wax and wane with the 11-year sunspot cycle. Observation of the aurorae can also tell us something about the earth's magnetic field and about atmospheric composition at high levels.

The aurorae are usually found only at high latitudes, unlike the much less spectacular and perhaps unfamiliar phenomenon known as the night *airglow*. In the absence of moonlight, it is responsible for most of the faint light we receive from the night sky. The airglow does not vary greatly with latitude and is completely independent of moon or starlight since it comes from the upper atmosphere. Although very faint, the total light from the airglow is much brighter than all the starlight together. Estimates are that the airglow provides the same visible illumination that one would receive from a candle at a distance equal to the length of a football field. The airglow is much stronger in invisible infrared radiation than in the visible wavelengths.

Another important phenomenon of the upper atmosphere is *atmospheric escape*. High above the earth, at the edge of interplanetary space, is the very top of our atmosphere, which is called the *exosphere*. In the exosphere, several hundred kilometers above the earth's surface, molecules are very far apart, and collisions are infrequent. Some molecules will acquire enough velocity to escape from the exosphere and shoot off into space, just as a rocket to the moon must reach escape velocity. It is due to this phenomenon of asmospheric escape that both the moon and Mercury have virtually no atmosphere at all. They have much weaker gravitational fields than the earth, and long ago their atmospheres escaped into space. This phenomenon also explains why Mars' atmosphere is much less dense than that of the earth. It is of the utmost importance to know at what rate molecules are escaping the earth's attraction. Are we in any danger of losing our own atmosphere?

II

How We Observe
the Upper Atmosphere

Back around the turn of the century, at the time of Teisserenc de Bort, there were three important methods for making measurements in the lower atmosphere none of which was suitable for the upper atmosphere. Kites, manned balloons, and unmanned balloons were used but because radio had not been perfected, the recovery of the equipment was an absolute necessity. While kites and manned balloons solved this problem, the heights they could reach were severely limited. The record for a kite was about 10 km, and one could never count on sufficient ground wind for flying. Besides being dangerous, manned balloons seldom exceeded the 5- to 8-km level.

The unmanned balloon, employed extensively by Teisserenc, could rise up into the lower stratosphere, but there was no assurance that the equipment would be recovered. Small rewards were even given for the return of instruments. Improved balloons still play a very important part in atmospheric observation today. Ascents often reach 30 km, but this ceiling still leaves much of the upper atmosphere unexplored. Since observations can be radioed back to the ground, the recovery of the equipment is no longer scientifically essential.

Measurements from Rockets

One of the major advantages of the balloon in atmospheric research is the fact that it may remain aloft for hours, thus permitting sustained data taking. At the end of World War II, the United States acquired a vehicle for atmospheric research which sacrificed long duration for greater altitude, and it revolutionized upper-atmospheric studies. With the fall of Nazi Germany, the United States captured parts for about one hundred V-2 rockets, a great many of which were promptly scheduled for upper-air research. (The first of 67 shots was made in March of 1946.)

The V-2, of course, was designed as a military rocket, not a research vehicle. However, its availability and its superiority over the only U.S.-developed rocket then available (the WAC Corporal) made its use in upper-air research only natural. The V-2 could carry a ton of equipment to a height of 160 km, while the Corporal, with only a 25-pound payload, had a peak altitude in the vicinity of 65 km. Consequently, the Corporal was never used extensively, except rarely as a second stage fired from a larger rocket in extreme high altitude research.

When its original German warhead was replaced by special nose sections designed for upper-air research, the V-2 was 46½ feet long; it had a diameter of 5 feet 5 inches. With payload, the V-2 weighed 14 or 15 tons. In direct contrast, the Corporal was 16 feet long, 12 inches in diameter, and weighed less than 700 pounds at launching. As mentioned before, the V-2 was *not* designed for atmospheric research. It was often necessary to load a V-2 with as much as a ton of ballast in order to stabilize its flight, so that it would be useful for research. The supply of V-2's available for research ran out late in 1952.

Near the end of 1947, an American-developed rocket useful in upper-atmospheric research became available. This was the Aerobee, essentially an improved version of the WAC Corporal. With a payload of 150 pounds, the original booster-launched Aerobee was capable of reaching heights above 100 km (later versions could go much higher) and many Aerobees were used throughout the 1950s. In fact, variations on the original Aerobee (for instance, the Aerobee 150) are still being used today.

The Viking, a rocket comparable in size to the V-2, was first used in upper-air research early in 1949. It could carry a payload as heavy as 500 to 1,000 pounds to altitudes exceeding 200 km. Unfortunately, however, the very high cost of the Viking made its extensive use in atmospheric research impractical and few were used. Whereas an Aerobee cost in the vicinity of $30,000 and the Deacon rockoon system, a balloon-launched rocket, less than $2,000, a single Viking rocket cost between $300,000 and $400,000. A relatively inexpensive rocket is very advantageous, since it permits more flights and thus more measurements.

One of the primary problems in the use of rockets for making measurements is the short flight time. While a balloon may stay up for hours, a rocket's flight is measured in terms of minutes. Thus, only a few observations can be made. Also, and perhaps more important, the speed at which a rocket travels makes atmospheric measurements very difficult.

Most of the information from a research rocket is in the form of radio signals, which are sent to ground-based receiving stations. In some few cases, the scientific equipment must be recovered, and in these cases it can be ejected and allowed to descend by parachute. In still other cases, the measurements are actually made by equipment descending on a parachute and radioing the results to the ground during the descent (or, for wind measurement, being tracked by ground radar). The last method has been used extensively during recent years with the small "meteorological rockets" like the Loki and the Arcas. These eject their packages at an altitude of 60 to 80 km so that measurements can be made in the mesosphere and upper stratosphere during the descent of the parachute.

Since the beginning of their use for research in 1946, rockets have been utilized to observe many different properties of the upper atmosphere. Density, composition, ionization, and wind are some of the properties that have been measured. We will discuss all these applications later when the subjects themselves are discussed.

An additional disadvantage in the use of rockets is that they cannot be fired near inhabited areas. If there is a remote chance that a rocket might land in an inhabited area, a shot cannot be made. Research launchings, therefore, are restricted to such areas as White Sands Proving Grounds, in southern New Mexico, and Fort Churchill in Canada, or from ships at sea. Because of cost and hazards of launching, rockets may never make as many soundings in the upper atmosphere as balloons now do in the troposphere and lower stratosphere. However, their use will undoubtedly increase.

Measurements from Satellites

Since 1957, artificial satellites have played a very important part in making upper-atmospheric measurements. A satellite can stay aloft for months, or even years, circling the earth once every 100 minutes or so, depending on its altitude. Since the satellite can radio its observations to ground receiving stations, a wealth of information may be obtained from each satellite.

However, the satellite has its limitations for upper-atmospheric research. As in the case of the rocket, its tremendous speed (about 17,000 miles per hour) makes direct on-board measurements rather complicated. Furthermore, satellites are limited to altitudes above about 200 km, for at lower altitudes, where the air density is higher, a satellite is slowed down by friction with the air and cannot remain in orbit. On the other hand, satellites orbiting at altitudes above 200 km are often used to study conditions at lower levels. Perhaps the best known example of this is the "weather" satellite, Tiros or Nimbus, which takes pictures of clouds from above and transmits these pictures to the ground.

Ground-based Measurements

The importance of direct measurements from rockets and, more recently, from satellites cannot be underestimated. But the reader must realize that much was known about the upper atmosphere in the pre-rocket days, even above the ceiling of balloons, as a result of many ingenious methods of making obser-

vations from the ground. We shall cover a number of
these, partly because some of them are still used, and
partly because they illustrate how scientists can make
important deductions from observations that are indirect and far from ideal.

By 1920, Teisserenc de Bort's assertion that the
temperature remains nearly constant with height
above the tropopause had gained firm acceptance. In
fact, there were many theories to explain why this
must be so. But the theoreticians were due for another
surprise. In late 1922, two British scientists, F. A.
Lindemann and G. M. B. Dobson, advanced the as-
tonishing theory that at some level above the tropopause the temperature must begin to *increase* with
altitude and eventually become as high as or higher
than the temperature at the earth's surface!

This theory was based on a careful study of meteor
trails. As mentioned before, these trails result from the
vaporization or "burning up" of meteors as they enter
the upper atmosphere at high speeds. This is the same
effect that causes so much trouble during the re-entry
of manned capsules, and requires elaborate precautions such as "heat shields." Now, to the casual observer, one meteor trail looks very much like another
one. And it might seem unlikely that these fleeting
flashes of light could be of use in scientific research.
But scientists are not "casual observers," and a group
led by W. F. Denning had learned much about meteor
trails as a result of careful observation. Among other
things, they learned the altitudes at which certain
meteor trails appeared and disappeared, and learned
also the speeds of the meteors. F. A. Lindemann and
G. M. B. Dobson were able to deduce, from theory
and from these observations, that the air densities at

those altitudes, between 50 and 100 km, were much higher than had previously been supposed.

In order to understand what this means in terms of temperature, it is necessary to consider what is known as the *hydrostatic equation,* which will be covered more fully in Chapter 5. We know that pressure and density decrease as we go upward; if they did not, the denser air at the top would sink and the less dense air at the bottom would rise. The hydrostatic equation tells the *rate* at which this decrease takes place. This rate depends on temperature, and the decrease is more rapid in *cold* air than in warm air. Lindemann and Dobson knew the altitude and density at the tropopause, and they deduced the density at the altitudes of the meteor trails. When they compared these figures with the hydrostatic equation, they found that the average temperature between the tropopause and the region of the meteor trails must be very much higher than the balloon measurements showed at, say, 10 to 15 km. They inferred then that at some higher elevation the temperature must increase with altitude in order to give such a high average. Later observation showed them to be absolutely right, and their work is a milestone in early studies of the upper atmosphere.

The suggestion of a region in the upper atmosphere where temperature increases with height received rapid support from another British scientist, F. J. W. Whipple, who had been concerned with a different problem which could be explained by this suggestion. This problem involved what is known as the "anomalous propagation of sound."

The anomalous or "abnormal" propagation of sound was observed on the occasion of the funeral of Queen

Victoria in 1901. The guns fired in the late Queen's honor were heard far to the north of London. The phenomenon was once again experienced during World War I, when gunfire from the battlefront in France could often be heard on the other side of the English Channel.

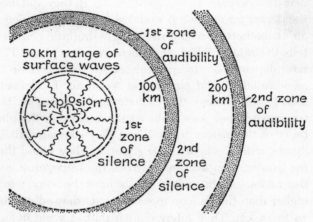

Figure 3. The Anomalous Propagation of Sound

When sound is anomalously propagated, an explosion can be heard at a distance far beyond the range of the direct sound waves. There is also a zone of silence in between. There may be one or more zones of audibility beyond the first zone, with more silent zones separating them. The zones of audibility are found in the form of rings. Figure 3 illustrates these zones for an explosion which has two anomalous zones of audibility.

It was soon determined that this phenomenon must be caused by refraction or "bending" of the sound by the earth's atmosphere. The big question remained, however: Where did this refraction take place and what caused it? There were three answers proposed: that the refraction was caused by changes in wind velocity with altitude, by a change in the composition of the earth's atmosphere with height, or by an ascending increase in temperature.

A change in wind velocity would cause anomalous propagation in only one direction. Sometimes zones of audibility occurred in roughly circular rings around the sound source. So wind could not be the only cause, although we now know that it does have some effect.

The second alternative, that of change of atmospheric constituents, was considered seriously at first. An increased proportion of lighter gases at higher altitudes could have accounted for the anomalous propagation. However, it was thought then and has since been verified by measurements that the composition of the atmosphere is essentially constant (ozone occurs only in very small proportions) up to a height of at least 80 km.

Only the third theory, that of increasing temperature, remains. It was this that Professor Whipple, after reading the work of Lindemann and Dobson, proposed as an explanation to the problem. The pieces of the puzzle fitted perfectly. The suggested increase in temperature in the upper atmosphere and the observed anomalous propagation of sound were consistent with each other.

But how does an increase in temperature cause the propagation of sound? To begin with, sound is a wave phenomenon. That is, it causes a wave pattern of vibration of molecules through the atmosphere. These spread out from their source in all directions, but any small portion of the wave front ordinarily travels in a straight line. Now, the speed of sound is greater when the temperature is higher. It is this characteristic which causes the anomalous propagation of sound through the temperature rise in the stratosphere.

When sound travels into colder air at an angle, the top part of each wave front travels more slowly than the bottom, causing the wave to refract upward. This effect is shown in Figure 4. Of course, when tempera-

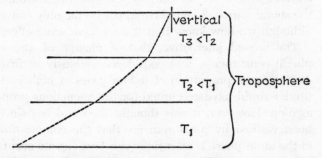

Figure 4. The Refraction of Sound Waves in the Troposphere

ture is constant, there is no refraction. When the temperature increases in front of the wave, the reverse happens. The top of the wave front is moving faster than the bottom, and the sound is refracted downward. This effect is demonstrated in Figure 5. Thus, a sound wave that travels into the upper stratosphere at a small enough angle, say 20° or less, will be refracted back to earth. Not much of the total sound is refracted because much of the sound will enter this zone at too large an angle and will still be rising when it enters the region of temperature drop in the mesosphere. The temperature rise in the thermosphere, above 80 km, has been known to cause anomalous propagation of

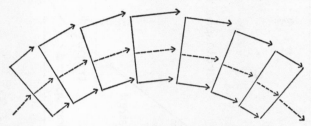

Figure 5. The Downward Refraction of Sound Waves

sound, but this is very rare. It must be remembered, too, that much of the sound travels out along the earth's surface and is eventually dissipated. Figure 6 presents an idealized diagram of the path of sound waves which are anomalously propagated.

The study of meteor trails and of the anomalous propagation of sound were the two major sources of information about the temperature structure of the upper atmosphere until the advent of rockets. The sound studies, refined to give also some information about wind, were utilized extensively even during the 1950s. By the use of these two tools, scientists knew that there was a temperature maximum near 50 km long before they were able to obtain any direct measurements from that altitude.

Another example of a ground-based measurement, which is still extensively used, is the probing of the ionosphere with radio waves. The fascinating story of this method began in 1901 when a radio signal transmitted from Cornwall, England, was detected by Marconi across the Atlantic Ocean in Newfoundland! Radio waves, like sound waves, travel in straight lines unless they are somehow bent or refracted by the atmosphere. Because of the earth's curvature, a radio

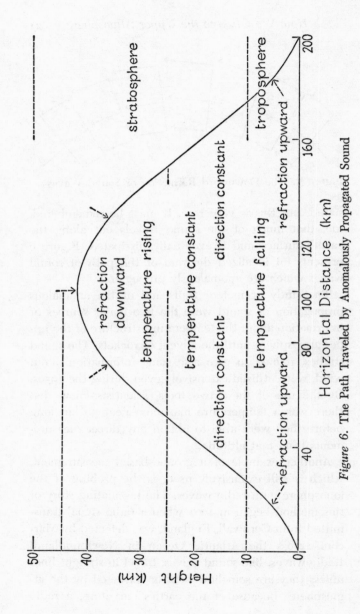

Figure 6. The Path Traveled by Anomalously Propagated Sound

signal could not travel across the Atlantic Ocean unless it were refracted or reflected. What was the cause of the refraction? In 1902 an American scientist, A. E. Kennelly, and a British scientist, Oliver Heaviside, independently suggested that this refraction could have been caused by a layer of free electrons in the upper atmosphere. However, it was not until 1925 that Sir Edward Appleton and M. A. F. Barnett of Great Britain demonstrated by a careful experiment that this was indeed the case.

We shall say a great deal more about the ionosphere and the refraction of radio waves in Chapter 6. Much of this information has been gained by experiments performed with ground-based equipment. A pulse of radio energy is transmitted upward and is observed again at the ground after its reflection by the ionosphere. It turns out that pulses of different frequency are reflected by layers of different electron density. The higher the frequency, the greater the electron density must be to cause reflection. In fact, if the frequency is too high the pulse passes through the atmosphere. By observing the range of frequencies that are reflected, it is possible to deduce the range of electron densities at the different levels in the ionosphere. Furthermore, the pulse can be timed—that is, the time required for it to travel up to the reflecting layer and back down again can be measured. This, together with the estimated speed of the pulse, which is less in the ionosphere than in a vacuum, gives information about the height of the reflecting layer.

Finally, we should not leave the subject of ground-based observations without mentioning the information that can be obtained from careful study of the light in the aurora and airglow. This light is emitted by the gases of the upper atmosphere. Each gas at low pressure when stimulated gives off light only at wavelengths or colors that are characteristic of that gas. This is different, for example, from the filament of an incandescent light bulb, which gives off light in a wide range of wavelengths centered in the yellow.

The property of gaseous emission is very important for studies of the upper atmosphere. The scientist can receive this light at the ground and determine by means of an instrument called a "spectrograph" exactly what wavelengths are coming from the upper atmosphere. He can then compare these with the emitting properties of different gases as determined from theory or laboratory experiments. If he finds that certain wavelengths coming from the upper atmosphere are the same as those that he knows come from a particular gas, then he can be sure that that gas must be present in the upper atmosphere. This general type of investigation is called "spectroscopic analysis."

Let us take a particular example. Both the airglow and the aurora contain light at the wavelength 5577 A (a greenish color) and also at the wavelength 6332 A (a reddish color). The only gas that can give off light at exactly these two wavelengths is oxygen in atomic form. Now practically all of the oxygen in our lower atmosphere is in molecular form—it consists of two oxygen atoms bound together in a molecule and called O_2. But the light from the aurora and airglow shows that in the upper atmosphere many of the oxygen molecules must be broken up into individual atoms (O) which radiate these two wavelengths. Until a few years ago, this was our only direct observational evidence for the presence of atomic oxygen in the upper atmosphere, although there were good theoretical reasons for expecting its presence, as will be discussed in Chapter 5.

Other examples of gases whose presence in the upper atmosphere has been detected by this method are atomic nitrogen, hydroxyl, and sodium. Atomic nitrogen (N) comes from the breaking up of nitrogen molecules (N_2), hydroxyl (OH) comes from the breaking up of water molecules (H_2O), but the presence of sodium (Na) is still something of a mystery. The most popular theory at present is that it is part of the residue left in the upper atmosphere by vaporized meteors.

We shall turn now in the succeeding chapters to the question of what has been learned by these and other observational techniques. However, one point should be emphasized here at the beginning. Studies of the upper atmosphere are still in a very active stage, and there are still many unsolved problems. Scientific publications contain each year literally thousands of pages devoted to new observations, theories, and conclusions about the upper atmosphere. Some of what seemed to be true a year or two ago has now been modified or even changed by later work. Some of what seems to be true now may very well be modified or even changed in the next few years. This is part of the excitement of scientific research, and it is especially present in upper-atmospheric research. No conclusion or theory is so sacred that it can stand for long in the face of contradictory evidence from new observations or experiments.

III

The Temperature
of the Upper Atmosphere

After this brief general look at the upper atmosphere let us now explore in more detail some of its characteristics. As a beginning point in science it is often helpful to have a simplified picture or model in mind which can then be modified as more is learned. Students of the atmosphere have such a model, which is called the "standard atmosphere." The "standard" represents an average of temperature over all latitudes and for all seasons. The graph of Figure 1 represents the variation of temperature with height of the standard atmosphere.

This model atmosphere is revised periodically as new information becomes available. For instance there has been a standard atmosphere for the troposphere and the lower stratosphere for many decades but the first attempt to include the upper atmosphere above 30 km was in 1947. This showed the temperature at a height of 50 to 60 km to be about 80°C. Not long afterward it was determined to be only about 0°C to 10°C and, of course, the necessary changes have been made in the standard atmosphere. The continued use of rockets and satellites has also suggested other changes and, especially above 80 km, it seems likely that still more revisions will be necessary in the years ahead.

The Lower Stratosphere

That part of the atmosphere extending from the tropopause to about 30 km, where the temperature begins to increase, we call the *lower stratosphere*. It has been observed extensively with the use of balloons. In fact, twice each day measurements are made at a network of over a thousand stations throughout the world, by the Weather Services of the various countries, and the results are widely disseminated by teletype for use in forecasting and research.

In the standard atmosphere (Figure 1) we see that the lower stratosphere is represented by a vertical line, representing a vertically constant temperature ("isothermal layer"). But worldwide measurements show that there are wide variations in the lower stratosphere, and that this representation simplifies the real picture quite drastically.

The bottom of the isothermal layer shown in the standard atmosphere is at 11 km, but this is only an average value. As mentioned in Chapter 1, the base of the lower stratosphere (the tropopause) is much higher in equatorial regions than in middle and high latitudes. This fact has the interesting consequence that the temperature at about 16 km above the earth's surface at the equator is actually *lower* than over the *poles*, as we can easily see by doing a simple calculation.

Near the poles, the average temperature at the ground is about 0°C, and the temperature decreases upward in the troposphere at the rate of about 6°C for each kilometer. So if the tropopause is at 6 km, the temperature at that altitude is about −36°C. Above the tropopause the temperature is nearly constant so at 16 km it is still about −36°C. Near the equator the average temperature at the ground is about 25°C. However, the tropopause is at 16 km. Then 6°C per kilometer × 16 kilometers equals 96°C. If we subtract this from the 25°C surface temperature, we get a temperature at 16 km of −71°C. Our usual conception that the temperature is necessarily higher near the equator than near the poles is true only for surface conditions! In the upper atmosphere, the opposite is sometimes true.

Meteorological conditions in the lower stratosphere vary markedly from summer to winter. In summer, we find a very dull situation. At a given place the temperature and wind change very little from one day to the next. Forecasters will have no serious problem in forecasting for stratospheric air travel in the summer. All they will have to do is measure the conditions today and forecast the same thing for the next day (or several days) and they will usually be right.

In winter, on the other hand, the lower stratosphere is the scene of some very interesting and remarkable meteorological variations. In January of 1952 a German meteorologist, Professor R. Scherhag, was making a series of very careful balloon measurements over Berlin. In those days, balloons usually burst at about 15 to 20 km and measurements at higher levels were quite scarce. However, Scherhag and his group, using special balloons and handling them very carefully, were getting measurements up to nearly 30 km. One day in late January he found to his astonishment that the temperature at 25 to 30 km was about 40°C higher than it had been only the day before. He termed this phenomenon *"explosionsartigen erwarmungen"* (explosive-type warming).

Since the late 1950s, improved balloons reach 30 km quite regularly and we now know from the study of many observations extending over many winters, that explosive-type warmings occur each winter. However, they do not always occur at the same time and place, and in some winters they are not as pronounced as the one observed by Scherhag. Their cause is not fully understood, but it seems that they are symptomatic of a large-scale change in the atmosphere's circulation patterns. Before the warming, winds in the lower stratosphere are usually very strong and from the west; afterward they are usually much weaker and sometimes even switch to the east.

The Upper Stratosphere

The *upper stratosphere* begins at about 30 km, where the rise in temperature becomes pronounced (see Figure 1). It ends at the *stratopause*, where the temperature stops increasing, at a height of about 50 km. Ground-based measurements of the stratosphere, as from the anomalous propagation of sound, have already been described.

There are several methods by which measurements can be made in the upper stratosphere with the use of rockets. One of these is the falling-sphere method, in which a sphere is ejected from a rocket near the top of its trajectory. Attracted by the earth's gravity, it starts falling toward the ground. However, because of friction with the air (often called "drag"), there is a limit to how fast it can fall. Furthermore, as it falls into the lower, denser air the drag increases and the sphere slows down. If the velocities and accelerations of the sphere are determined, as with a ground-based radar set, then the density of the air can be deduced at each elevation. Knowing the density at each altitude, scientists can determine the temperature from two equations, the hydrostatic equation mentioned in Chapter 2 and the "equation of state," which relates air temperature, air density, and air pressure. This equation will be covered in more detail in Chapter 5.

Rockets may also eject instrument packages, which descend slowly on parachutes and radio information to ground stations. For example, there are now instruments that measure temperature on the way down through the upper stratosphere by means of a "thermistor," an electrical resistor whose resistance changes as the temperature changes. Furthermore, the parachute drifts horizontally with the wind as it falls and can be tracked by radar to determine the wind speed and direction.

Some rockets eject "chaff," which consists of a large number of small metal or metal-coated nylon strips, which have been called "metallized confetti." The payload of a Loki II rocket consists of more than a million pieces of chaff. The chaff moves with the wind as it falls and, like the parachute mentioned above, can be tracked by radar for information about wind speed and direction.

Another observational technique is the rocket-grenade method. The rocket fires a series of grenades, usually at intervals of a few kilometers, as it climbs. Microphones are set up on the ground, almost directly below the explosions, and are used to determine the exact time and angle of arrival of the sound wave from each explosion. This information is enough to determine average wind and temperature in each layer (a few kilometers thick) between two explosions. The exact method of reducing the data is quite complicated, but it takes into account the fact that the sound waves drift with the wind and also travel faster in layers where the temperature is higher.

Both the rocket-grenade and the falling-sphere methods can be used in the mesosphere as well as in the upper stratosphere.

Why does the temperature increase with altitude in the upper stratosphere? As mentioned in Chapter 1, the answer lies in the ozone content of this part of the atmosphere. Ozone (O_3) is a minor constituent of the atmosphere, present only in very small amounts. However, it is an extremely important one. The ozone density or the number of grams or number of molecules of ozone in a given volume is greatest at about 20 to 25 km. Its *relative* density, compared with the air density in the same volume, is greatest at about 30 km, although some ozone is found as high as 80 km and as low as the ground.

Ozone's importance lies in its ability to absorb the sun's ultraviolet radiation in the wavelengths between 2000 A and 3000 A. These wavelengths are absorbed only very slightly by the oxygen and nitrogen higher in the atmosphere. The solar energy absorbed by ozone is changed to heat and causes the temperature to rise in the upper stratosphere.

But why, you might ask, is the temperature higher at 50 km than at 25 km, where the ozone density is greater? There are two reasons. The first is the progressive diminution of the ultraviolet rays by ozone absorption. Very few of the ultraviolet rays ever reach the 25-km level, since most have already been absorbed above. The second reason lies in the relation between heat, density, and temperature. When heat is added to a substance, such as a volume of air molecules, the temperature increases. However, for the same amount of heat, the temperature increases more when the substance is less dense (that is, has less mass). For example, the amount of heat required to bring one quart of water to boiling (100°C) would not be enough to bring two quarts to the same temperature. Now the air density at 50 km is much less than at 25 km, so even a smaller amount of ozone and a smaller amount of heat causes a higher temperature at this higher elevation.

The stratopause, the region of maximum temperature at the top of the stratosphere, is usually found at an altitude of about 50 km. Although its exact altitude and temperature do vary with latitude and season, this variation is not yet known in great detail. It appears to be less than the variations found for the tropopause.

The Mesosphere

The mesosphere, like the troposphere, is a layer where temperature decreases with altitude. Its base is at the stratopause, and it extends up to a height of about 80 km. At the *mesopause,* which is the name for the top of the mesosphere, atmospheric temperature reaches its lowest value, about −90°C on the average but sometimes as low as −130°C. Above the mesopause, in the thermosphere, the temperature starts rising again, as will be discussed later in this chapter.

Obviously, direct measurements of conditions in the mesosphere must be made with the aid of rockets. The two methods most commonly used are the falling-sphere and rocket-grenade methods, both of which were described earlier in this chapter. Of course, before the advent of rockets indirect methods had to be used to gather information about the mesosphere. The use of meteor observations was discussed in Chapter 2.

The biggest mystery about the mesosphere concerns the peculiar seasonal temperature variations at high latitudes. In the upper mesosphere at high latitudes the observed temperatures are *higher* in the winter than they are in the summer. In fact, they are even higher than the summer temperatures at lower latitudes. This occurs in spite of the fact that the sun is at or below the horizon at high latitudes in winter. This surprising temperature variation has still not been explained satisfactorily. It seems likely that the final answer will have to involve some kind of atmospheric circulation, carrying heat poleward from lower latitudes in winter.

The altitude of the mesopause seems to be fairly constant in contrast to the tropopause and stratopause. However, as indicated above, in connection with the high temperatures the mesopause is rather ill defined at high latitudes in winter. For example, some rocket-grenade soundings at Fort Churchill, Canada (59°N), have even shown a small layer of temperature *maximum* in the vicinity of 80 km. Figure 7 shows an example. Remember that in the standard atmosphere and in other measurements, the temperature falls continuously as the 80-km level is approached.

The usually low temperatures in the mesosphere and near the mesopause result from the lack of ultra-

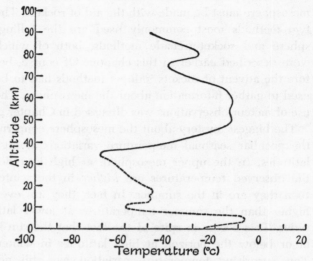

Figure 7. The 8o-Kilometer Temperature Maximum at
High Latitude. This figure shows the temperature above Fort Churchill, Canada (59°N), on
January 27, 1958. The dashed line represents
information gathered from balloon soundings,
the solid line that gained from rocket-grenade
soundings.

violet absorption in this layer of the atmosphere.
There is little ozone present, so there is little absorption of ultraviolet radiation of wavelengths between
2000 A and 3000 A. Most of the ultraviolet radiation
at wavelengths less than 2000 A has already been absorbed in the thermosphere by oxygen and nitrogen.
Since part of the sun's ultraviolet radiation cannot be
absorbed by the gases in the mesosphere and the rest
never even gets there, the mesosphere has a low temperature.

Winds in the Stratosphere and Mesosphere

Although this chapter is devoted mainly to the temperature structure of the upper atmosphere, we can appropriately mention here some interesting facts about the wind systems of the stratosphere and mesosphere. Wind information has been obtained from balloons, from the rocket-grenade experiment, and from the radar tracking of chaff and parachutes dropped from meteorological rockets, as discussed earlier.

During the summer, easterly winds (winds blowing from the east toward the west) occur throughout most of the stratosphere and mesosphere. They have their maximum speed of about 60 meters per second near the stratopause in the vicinity of 30° latitude. These winds are remarkably steady. At all locations in the summer hemisphere they blow very nearly from the east with very little north-south component, and they change hardly at all from one day to the next. These unchanging easterlies make up part of the "dull" summertime situation that we remarked upon earlier in this chapter.

During the winter months, the situation is quite different. The winds blow, on the average, from the west and are generally stronger than during the summer season; speeds of more than 100 meters per second are quite common, especially in the lower mesosphere in middle latitudes. However, the wintertime winds are very variable. There are occasions when the west winds become weak and may even change to easterlies. Sometimes this occurs over limited areas and occasionally, in connection with a major stratospheric warming, over most of the hemisphere.

This reversal of wind direction between summer and winter does not apply to a region of the earth near the equator. There, between about 15°N and 15°S, a very peculiar and surprising wind behavior has been observed. The winds are predominantly east for 12 or 13 months and then predominantly west for the next 12 or 13 months. This phenomenon has been termed the "26-month equatorial stratospheric wind oscillation," because if the wind is east in one month it will likely be west 13 months later and east again 26 months later. The oscillation is strongest at about 30 km, and is weak near the tropopause and stratopause. Because of the scarcity of balloon observations in the stratosphere at low latitudes, the equatorial stratospheric wind oscillation was not discovered until about 1960. It has no explanation and presents one more puzzle for the meteorologist and aeronomer, the name often given to a scientist who studies the upper atmosphere.

The Thermosphere

Returning now to our survey of the atmosphere's temperature structure, let us consider the thermosphere, which stretches from the mesopause to the "edge" of space. Although the thermosphere has a much greater vertical extent, 400 km or more depending on how one draws the line between "atmosphere" and "space," than any of the other layers, it contains only an extremely small proportion of the earth's atmosphere. In fact, less than 1/100,000th of the atmosphere's molecules are above the mesopause.

In the thermosphere, between 80 and 200 km, there are no direct measurements of temperature available, and only a few direct measurements of density. The falling-sphere and rocket-grenade methods do not work at this altitude. A few rockets have carried pressure-gauges up through this region, and these readings allow one to determine the air density. However, this is a difficult experiment and the results are not very precise.

On the other hand, there are a very large number of density measurements above about 200 km. These come from observations of the orbits of artificial satellites. If an artificial satellite circled the earth in a complete vacuum it would continue in the same orbit for an indefinitely long period of time, just as the earth has circled the sun and the moon has circled the earth for billions of years. But even the tiny amount of atmosphere encountered by an artificial satellite eventually slows the satellite down as a result of friction or "drag." As the satellite slows down, the gravitational attraction of the earth pulls it in closer and closer. It spirals inward, eventually plunging back toward earth and meeting a fiery death, just as meteors do.

Artificial satellites are very carefully observed by tracking stations all over the earth, and the details of their orbits are very accurately known. By observing how the orbits change, scientists can determine how much drag there is and therefore what the air density is at the levels where the satellite is moving. The air density in turn can be converted to temperatures, as explained earlier in the case of the falling-sphere methods.

All of these measurements show that the temperature begins to rise at the mesopause and continues to increase up to about 300 km, eventually reaching a value of about 1000°C or even higher. Above about

300 km the temperature is vertically constant at any one time and place. These extremely high temperatures are caused by absorption of the sun's ultraviolet light at wavelengths below 2000 A, primarily by oxygen and nitrogen. Although there is not much energy available from the sun at such very short wavelengths, neither is there much air to be heated, and a little energy goes a long way in affecting the temperature.

One very interesting aspect of the temperature of the thermosphere is its extreme variability. The temperature in the high-level isothermal layer above 300 km (sometimes called the "thermopause") can change from time to time by more than 1000°C. For example, it is several hundred degrees higher during the day when the sun is shining than at night. Furthermore, for a particular time of day, there is a wide variation over a period of years caused by changes in the amount of radiation given off by the sun. At a time called "sunspot-maximum" (see Chapter 4) when the sun gives off a maximum amount of radiation at the very short wavelengths, the temperature at midday may be as high as 2000°C. On the other hand, five or six years later at sunspot-minimum, the midday temperature may be as low as 700°C to 1000°C.

If temperatures in the thermosphere reach 1000°C and above, you might well wonder how satellites and astronauts can survive in this intense heat. The answer lies in the meaning of temperature and in the very low air density. Temperature is defined in terms of the average speed at which molecules are moving. At high temperatures, molecules travel very rapidly. As the temperature becomes lower, the molecules travel more and more slowly, until there is practically no motion near absolute zero. The heating of an object

Plate I
The solar corona photographed from Talkeetna, Alaska,
during the eclipse of July 20, 1963. (Courtesy of the High
Altitude Observatory, Boulder, Colorado.)

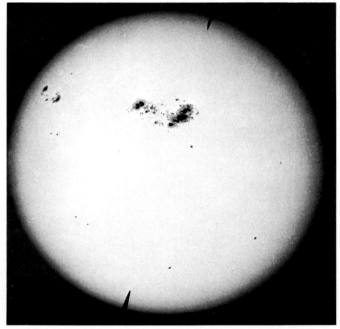

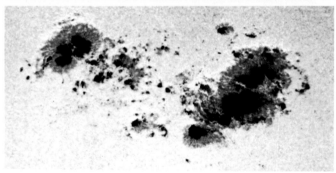

Plate II
The great sunspot group of April 7, 1947, shown as it appeared on the sun and also in enlargement. (Courtesy of the Mount Wilson and Palomar Observatories, Pasadena, California.)

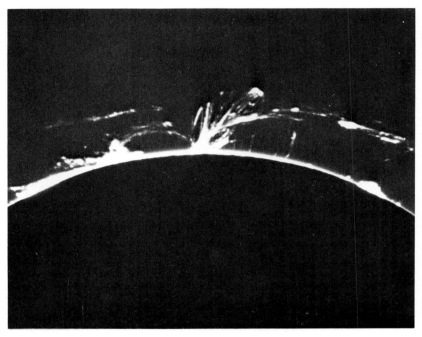

Plate III
Prominence in the vicinity of an active region on the sun,
photographed April 16, 1947. (Courtesy of the High
Altitude Observatory, Boulder, Colorado.)

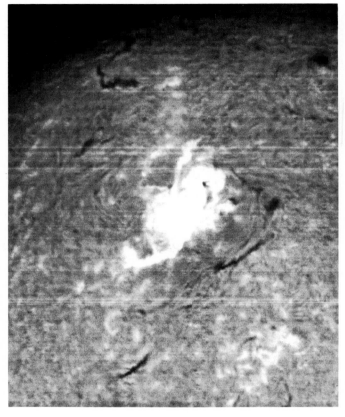

Plate IV
A solar flare photographed in the light of a hydrogen Fraunhofer line, July 16, 1959. (Courtesy of the Mount Wilson and Palomar Observatories, Pasadena, California.)

by conduction is caused by repeated collisions with rapidly moving outside molecules. These collisions excite the molecules of the object to more motion, thus resulting in a higher temperature.

The molecules in the thermosphere are moving at very high speeds, as the temperatures show. However, because atmospheric density is so low in the thermosphere, only a very few of the fast-moving air molecules collide with a foreign body, such as a satellite. Thus, because of the paucity of collisions, the temperature of the "atmosphere" outside it has little effect on the surface temperature of a satellite. Actually, because of the very low air density in the upper thermosphere, the effect of "temperature" as we know it does not exist. The major source of heating a satellite encounters is a direct result of radiation from the sun, which is controlled by the satellite's reflecting surface.

The Importance of the Sun and Solar Radiation

It should be obvious by now that the sun's radiation is of prime importance in the temperature structure of the atmosphere. The high temperatures in both the upper stratosphere and the thermosphere are a direct result of the absorption of the sun's ultraviolet rays, by ozone in the former case and by oxygen and nitrogen in the latter. The great variability in the sun's emission results in the extreme range of temperature in the thermosphere. And, of course, it is the sun that heats the troposphere, in which we live, although in this case indirectly as a result of convection and re-radiation of heat from the ground.

The sun also has profound effects on other aspects

of the upper atmosphere. It affects the composition, that is, the kind of gases that are present at different altitudes. It is responsible for the formation of the ionosphere. Particles from the sun cause the auroral displays.

For all these reasons, we shall pause temporarily in this survey of upper-atmospheric structure and in Chapter 4 discuss the sun, its radiation, and some of its effects on the upper atmosphere.

IV

The Sun and the
Upper Atmosphere

The point may seem too obvious to make, but it is nevertheless true that practically all the energy available to the earth's atmosphere and to man comes ultimately from the sun. The sun is only one among countless stars, and it is a rather small one at that. But we are so much closer to it than to any of the others that the energy reaching us from the sun is incomparably greater than that coming from all the other stars together.

Solar energy comes to us through nearly empty space, mainly in the form of electromagnetic radiation. Electromagnetic radiation is familiar to you in many forms, such as light that you can see and heat that you can feel. It also includes X-rays, ultraviolet radiation, and radio waves. These different kinds of radiation may seem unrelated, but all are forms of a combined electric and magnetic field which can move through empty space with the speed of light, about 300,000,000 or 3×10^8 meters per second, and through some kinds of matter with a somewhat lower speed. The different kinds of radiation are often described in terms of "wavelength," which is the distance between consecutive points where the electric field (or the magnetic field) is at a maximum. Table 1 shows the names given to different wavelength regions, although the points of division between these regions are not really very clear cut.

Solar radiation comes in a wide spectrum of wavelengths, but with different intensity in different parts of the spectrum. About 40 per cent of the energy is concentrated in the visible part of the spectrum, the part detectable by the human eye, between 4000 and 7000 A. About 50 per cent is contained in the longer wavelengths, and only about 10 per cent in the shorter ones.

For ordinary meteorological problems, scientists are naturally concerned with the very large amount of solar energy found in the visible and longer wavelengths. Some of this energy is reflected back to space by clouds and some by the air itself. Of that which is not reflected, most manages to get through our atmosphere and reach the earth's surface, where it provides the energy needed to power the main part of the atmosphere—producing the wind systems, storms, and evaporation-precipitation cycle in which meteorologists, and non-scientists as well, are mainly interested. The details of these meteorological processes present

TABLE 1
NAMES OF DIFFERENT REGIONS OF THE
ELECTROMAGNETIC SPECTRUM

Wavelength*	Name	Comments
Less than 100 A	X-ray	Short-wavelength X-rays are called "hard" X-rays, and long-wavelength X-rays are called "soft" X-rays.
100 A to 4000 A	Ultraviolet	Wavelengths between 100 and 1000 A are sometimes called "extreme ultraviolet," or EUV; wavelengths between 3000 and 4000 A are sometimes called "near ultraviolet."
4000 A to 7000 A	Visible	Colors as detected by the human eye range from violet at the short-wavelength end to red at the long-wavelength end of the visible.
7000 A to 10,000,000 A (0.7 μ to 1000 μ)	Infrared	Short wavelengths, say up to 3 μ, are sometimes called "near infrared," and longer wavelengths, say beyond 20 μ, are sometimes called "far infrared."
1000 μ to 1,000,000 μ (0.1 cm to 100 cm)	Microwave	Includes ordinary radar at 1 cm to 10 cm.
Greater than 100 cm	Radio	Standard broadcast band at 200 to 600 m.

* Wavelengths are expressed in different units. 1 Angstrom (symbol A) is 10^{-8} cm. 1 micron (symbol μ) is 10^{-4} cm.

many interesting problems, which are far from being solved, but which are not the ones that we have set out to discuss in this book. We are concerned with the upper atmosphere, where the energy source and the related problems are quite different.

The first and foremost point to keep in mind is that the upper atmosphere directly absorbs all the solar radiation with wavelength less than about 3000 A. This energy never reaches the ground, or even the top of the troposphere. Although the total amount of energy involved is only about 1 to 2 per cent of all the energy reaching the atmosphere from the sun, it is a lot relative to the upper atmosphere because the amount of air there is so small.

This special situation, that the upper atmosphere is powered by directly absorbed, short-wavelength radiation, leads to several problems that are not found in ordinary meteorology. First, since the energy that "runs" the upper atmosphere is all absorbed there, we are unable to detect it and measure it with instruments at the ground. Measurements must be made through the use of rockets or satellites that reach altitudes above most of the atmosphere. In the second place, we know that solar radiation at short enough wavelengths, especially at those less than 1000 A, does not remain constant with time. There are important variations over a period of about eleven years, and sometimes even from one day to the next. And thirdly, as was pointed out in Chapter 3, this variable, hard-to-measure radiation affects the air in many ways—for example, its temperature, its composition, and its ionization.

So, before we go into any more detail about the

upper atmosphere, it will be necessary to describe some of the things that we know about the sun and about its radiation.

The Sun

Let us begin with some simple facts about the sun. It is a vast rotating sphere of very hot gas, mostly hydrogen and helium. Its mass is about 2×10^{33} grams (about 4×10^{30} pounds), and the diameter of its visible disk is approximately 1.4×10^6 km. The earth moves around the sun once a year at an average distance of about 1.5×10^8 km (about 93,000,000 miles). It is interesting to compare these numbers with the mass and size of our earth. The sun's mass is 333,400 times that of the earth, its diameter about 100 times that of the earth, and its distance from us about 10,000 times the earth's diameter.

Just as the earth rotates about an imaginary axis through its North and South Poles, so does the sun. However, its period of rotation is much longer than that of the earth. As seen from the earth, the sun rotates once in about 26 of our days near the solar "equator," and this period increases to about 34 of our days near the solar "poles." This difference in rotation rate between equator and poles is possible because of the fact that the sun is not a solid object. A period of 27 days is often used as an average or effective period, because it applies to low solar latitudes, where much of the solar variability takes place.

The vast amount of energy that is continually being radiated away from the sun comes as a result of controlled nuclear reactions within the interior of the sun.

These reactions convert hydrogen into helium and at the same time change a small amount of the original hydrogen mass into energy. Thus the sun is continually "burning up" its hydrogen—not in the sense of the usual terrestrial "fire," but in the sense of a conversion of mass into energy, as in a hydrogen bomb. However, we should hasten to add that there is no danger of the sun's running out of hydrogen for many more billions of years, so great is its supply.

The temperature in the interior of the sun, where these nuclear reactions take place, is estimated to be in the vicinity of $2 \times 10^7 °C$. Fortunately, we are not directly exposed to so high a temperature. As energy moves away from the interior of the sun, it is absorbed and reemitted countless times, and the energy that finally escapes from the sun comes mostly from a relatively cool and relatively thin layer of gas called the *photosphere*.

The photosphere is often spoken of as the "surface" of the sun. It is not, however, a solid or liquid surface such as we find on earth. It is, rather, a layer of gas several hundred kilometers thick, from which comes most of the light that we are able to see. There is gas even above the photosphere, but it is so thin that it lets most of the visible radiation get through. The region extending for about 10,000 km above the photosphere is called the *chromosphere*. Still higher in the solar atmosphere is the *corona*, which shows up as a faint whitish halo around the main part of the sun during a solar eclipse. A photograph of the corona taken during the solar eclipse of July 20, 1963, is shown in Plate I.

Solar Radiation

The sun and how astronomers study it make a fascinating subject, but the part that most concerns us here has to do with the kind of radiation that reaches the earth and the extent to which this radiation varies from time to time. This is to say that we would like to know how much radiation reaches the top of the atmosphere at each and every wavelength.

The characteristics of solar radiation in the visible and infrared parts of the spectrum have been known for years as a result of measurements made at the earth's surface. Of course, allowance has to be made for what happens to the radiation as it comes through the atmosphere, but this can be done with reasonable accuracy. In brief, solar radiation is the most intense at about 4800 A, and the intensity falls off quite smoothly and gradually as the wavelength becomes larger or smaller than this value. The change of intensity with wavelength is illustrated in Figure 8. When the radiation changes smoothly and gradually in this manner scientists speak of a "continuous" spectrum, or a "continuum." This type of radiation comes from a solid object or from a gas at high pressure and temperature like the sun.

Figure 8 also contains a curve labeled "black body." The term "black body" is used in physics to refer to an ideal radiating object. Such an object, no matter what material it is made of and no matter whether it is solid, liquid, or gaseous, would give off radiation in a way that depends only on the temperature of the object. The black-body curve in Figure 8 shows what would be radiated by such an ideal object at a tem-

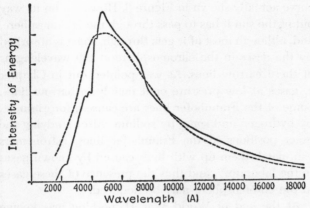

Figure 8. Solar Spectrum. The unbroken line represents the curve of spectral distribution of solar radiation. The broken line represents that of a black body at 6000°C. The curves show the relative amount of energy generated at each wavelength.

perature of 6000°C. This curve does not match the observed solar radiation exactly, but it fits well enough to enable us to deduce with considerable confidence that the temperature of the photosphere, from which this radiation comes, is about 6000°C.

There is one other important point concerning solar radiation in the visible and infrared. There are many very narrow regions, too narrow to be drawn in Figure 8, where the amount of radiation dips sharply at a particular wavelength. A continuous spectrum passes smoothly and gradually from color to color as the rainbow does. Under certain conditions thin black lines appear between colors. These are the dips in the curve of Figure 8. In the case of the solar spectrum, they are called *Fraunhofer lines.* When the radiation leaves the photosphere, it is continuous and looks like the curve actually shown in Figure 8. However, on its way out of the sun it has to pass through the chromosphere, and, although most of it gets through, some is absorbed by the gases in the chromosphere at the wavelengths of these narrow lines. As was pointed out in Chapter 2, gases at low pressure emit mainly in narrow lines. Some of the Fraunhofer lines are caused, for example, by hydrogen and some by sodium. After studying the exact positions of the Fraunhofer lines, astronomers can match them up with lines caused by known gases in the laboratory, and thus the presence of these gases in the chromosphere may be deduced.

At the end of World War II, nothing was known about the solar spectrum at wavelengths shorter than 3000 A because none of this radiation reaches the ground and so cannot be measured there. For lack of anything better, it was customary in those days to assume that the radiation at the shorter wavelengths was similar to radiation from a black body at 6000°C, just as is true in the visible region. One of the first experiments with the V-2 rockets was carried out to test this hypothesis. That experiment and many others since then have shown that this was a very poor assumption. As a result, many of our ideas about the upper atmosphere, if they depended on the amount of radiation coming from the sun, had to be changed and improved.

Without going into great detail about these experiments, let us summarize the most important results of the measurements. To begin with, at most wavelengths less than 3000 A there is much *less* radiation than would be expected from a black body at 6000°C. As a matter of fact, the reader may note from a close inspection of Figure 8 that this is true between 3000 and 4000 A; and it is even more pronounced at shorter wavelengths. Secondly, as the wavelength becomes shorter and shorter the energy tends to be concentrated more and more in narrow lines rather than in a continuum, indicating that this energy is coming from gases in the chromosphere and corona, which are at very low pressures. There is one particularly important line to which we shall refer later. This line is located at 1216 A and is radiated by the hydrogen in the chromosphere. It is called "Lyman alpha"— "Lyman" after the man who first observed it in the laboratory and "alpha" because it is the first of an interrelated series of lines. There is more energy radiated in this line, within 1 or 2 A wavelength, than at all other wavelengths less than about 1500 A put together. A third important result of the rocket and satellite measurements has been the acquiring of new knowledge about the X-ray radiation at wavelengths less than about 100 A. This radiation comes from the corona and is characteristic of gases at extremely low pressure and extremely high temperature. (The temperature of the corona is estimated to be about $1 \times 10^{6}°C$.) Coronal radiation is highly variable, and its changes from time to time cause many important changes in the upper atmosphere.

Table 2 summarizes some of this information about regions of the sun and the radiation coming from them.

Solar Variability

It has long been known that the sun's surface usually contains certain dark regions, which are known as *sunspots*. They were seen as early as 28 B.C. by the

TABLE 2
REGIONS OF THE SUN

Name	Approximate thickness	Comments
Interior	7×10^5 km	Source of solar energy; temperature near center 2×10^7°C.
Photosphere	5×10^2 km	Source of most radiation reaching the earth; temperature about 6000°C.
Chromosphere	5×10^3 km	Source of line emission in ultraviolet, such as Lyman alpha; temperature increases from 6000°C at bottom to about 1×10^6°C at top.
Corona	Indefinite; at least a few solar diameters	Source of X-rays; temperature about 1×10^6°C.

Chinese, who thought them due to flying birds. In 1610, Galileo Galilei observed them with his newly perfected telescope. He noticed that spots often appeared on the western edge of the sun (as seen from the earth), moved toward and past the central meridian, and finally disappeared at the eastern edge about 13 to 14 days later. He correctly deduced that the spots were fixed on the surface of the sun, which was rotating, as described earlier in this chapter. Sunspots may be so small that they are barely visible from the earth, or they may cover areas as large as 50,000 km in diameter, several times the diameter of the earth. Spots, once formed, may last only a day or two, or they may persist through several solar rotations. Plate II shows what a large group of sunspots looks like.

Sunspots have excited the imagination of scientists and laymen, because the average number of spots on the sun changes dramatically over a period of years. There are periods which are separated by about 11 years when spots are very numerous, but there are other times when very few are observed. This characteristic change is called the "sunspot cycle"—years with a large number of spots are called sunspot-maximum, and years with only a few spots sunspot-minimum. Figure 9 shows how the average number of sunspots has changed each year during the past 100 years. As this is being written, in 1966, we have just experienced a sunspot-minimum and expect the next maximum in the late 1960s.

Any regular change in the appearance of the sun suggests that there might be some corresponding change in solar radiation and therefore some change in our atmosphere. This presumption has led several scientists to look for 11-year periods in the weather, but no very clear-cut results have emerged. There are, however, very definite changes in the upper atmosphere—in the temperature of the thermosphere, in the number of electrons, and in the frequency of bright aurorae—which are caused by solar changes associated with the sunspots.

The changes of radiation that cause changes in the upper atmosphere cannot be traced directly to the sunspots themselves. However, a large sunspot group

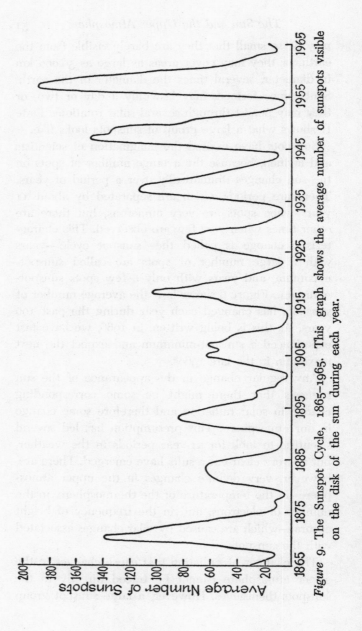

Figure 9. The Sunspot Cycle, 1865–1965. This graph shows the average number of sunspots visible on the disk of the sun during each year.

in the photosphere like the one shown in Plate II is the easily visible indicator of a region of solar disturbance, which extends from below the photosphere up through the chromosphere and into the corona. This is called an *active region.* In an active region there is a generally increased level of radiation from the chromosphere and corona, so that the very short-wave ultraviolet and X-ray radiation which comes from these parts of the sun is greater during periods when there are more sunspots and more active regions.

Plate III shows a photograph of a prominence in the vicinity of an active region. Prominences are large clouds of bright gas which extend outward from the chromosphere. The prominences near active regions, like the one shown in Plate III, show rapid changes of form and brightness and appear to represent the movement of vast masses of hot gas out of and into the chromosphere.

Active regions are sometimes the scene of intense, short-lived eruptions during which the level of radiation affecting our upper atmosphere rises abruptly for a few hours. Such an event is termed a *solar flare,* and it can be observed from the ground through the brightening of certain Fraunhofer lines in the visible part of the spectrum. Plate IV shows a solar flare photographed in the light of a hydrogen Fraunhofer line. The really large changes in solar radiation, however, take place in the X-rays coming from the corona, and these cause easily detectable and very important changes in our ionosphere. Furthermore, during a large solar flare, the sun ejects large numbers of material particles (electrons, protons) which reach the earth from an hour to a day or two later. The brightest aurorae are the result of the bombarding of the upper atmosphere by such particles.

Sunspots have been compared with the rash occurring in a case of measles. They are easily seen, but they are really only symptomatic of the important things that are happening. Some sunspot groups are associated with only very weak active regions that cause no important changes in the upper atmosphere. Nevertheless, the greater the number of sunspots, the more likely it is that our upper atmosphere will be disturbed by increased solar radiation and by particles coming from the sun.

But now let us return to earth and consider what else has been learned about our atmosphere.

V

Composition of the
Upper Atmosphere

Air as we know is composed of a mixture of several different gases and it changes very little from place to place or from time to time. Regardless of where you may live, you are breathing pretty much the same sort of air as any other human being breathes, or as your ancestors breathed, unless, of course, man has fouled the air near your home with pollutants. But as far as nature is concerned, the relative proportions of the gases in the air are about the

same everywhere near the ground, with one important exception. The exception is water vapor—water
in its invisible gaseous form. Water behaves differently
from other components of the atmosphere because it
can change very easily from a gas to a liquid or solid.
The percentage of water vapor in the air can change
from almost none when the air is very cold and dry to
as much as 3 per cent when the air is hot and humid.

Besides water vapor, the air near the ground contains the gases shown in Table 3. It is made up almost
wholly of nitrogen and oxygen, both in the form of
molecules containing two atoms each. Measurements
have shown that the percentages found in Table 3 remain the same everywhere near the surface and
throughout the troposphere. But what about the upper atmosphere? We shall see that there are important
changes in atmospheric composition at high elevations
and that attempting to discover which gases are present in what proportions is one of the most difficult
problems for the upper-atmosphere scientist.

TABLE 3
COMPOSITION OF DRY AIR NEAR SEA LEVEL

Gas	Proportion by volume (per cent)
Nitrogen (N_2)	78.084
Oxygen (O_2)	20.946
Argon (A)	0.934
Carbon dioxide (CO_2)	0.033
Neon (Ne)	0.00182
Helium (He)	0.00052
Others	0.00066

Mean Molecular Weight and the Hydrostatic Equation

We are anxious to know what gases are in the upper atmosphere for many reasons. One is that we need to know how heavy the molecules are on the average, in order to be able to determine the temperature of the air from measurements of pressure and density. This derivation involves some ideas that may not be familiar to the reader, but these ideas are so important that they need to be explained with the help of two simple equations.

One of these equations is called the "equation of state" and relates the pressure, temperature, and density of the air in any small volume of the atmosphere. According to this equation, the pressure is equal to the product of density, temperature, and a number called the "universal gas constant," all divided by the mean weight of the molecules. Using the common symbols, we can write this equation as

$$p = \frac{\rho \, T \, R}{m}$$

where p is pressure, ρ is density[3], T is temperature, R is the universal gas constant, whose value has been determined from laboratory studies, and m is the average weight of the molecules. In this equation, it is necessary to use the temperature in "degrees absolute" or "degrees Kelvin," which is obtained by adding 273° to the temperature in degrees centigrade. The molecular weight of nitrogen is 28 and that of oxygen

[3] ρ is the symbol for the Greek letter "rho" and is commonly used to stand for density.

is 32, on a scale in which one atom of oxygen weighs 16. Since the air near the ground is made up mostly of these two gases, we should expect m to lie between 28 and 32. Its actual value near the ground is 28.966.

The second equation is called the "hydrostatic equation" and it simply states that the weight of the air in a small volume is just balanced by the pressure forces acting on that air. Let us imagine a small "box" of air, as is shown in Figure 10, with the bottom of the box a distance z_1 above the ground, the top a distance z_2 above the ground, and the area of the top and bottom sides of the box each 1 square centimeter (abbreviated 1 cm^2). The volume of this imaginary box is $(z_2 - z_1) \times 1$ cm^2, and if the air density is still called ρ, the mass of air in the box equals $\rho (z_2 - z_1) \times 1$ cm^2. So the weight of this air is $\rho g (z_2 - z_1) \times 1$ cm^2, where g represents the force due to gravity acting on each gram of air in the box.

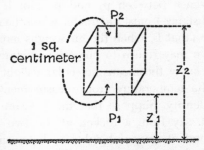

Figure 10. The Hydrostatic Equation. The weight of the air in the "box" is balanced by the difference between the pressure forces below and above.

The air, of course, does not fall toward the ground. It is held up by the pressure exerted on its lower side by all the air beneath it, as the arrow labeled p_1 represents in the picture. The force due to this pressure is equal to p_1 times the area of the bottom of the box, or $p_1 \times 1$ cm². There is also a force that acts in a downward direction on the top of the box, with a magnitude of $p_2 \times 1$ cm², due to the pressure exerted by the air above. The difference between these two pressure forces just balances the weight of the air; otherwise the box would move up or down. So we are finally able to write

$$(p_1 - p_2) = \rho g (z_2 - z_1)$$

We have omitted the factor of 1 cm², since it would appear on both sides of the equation.

This is the "hydrostatic equation," and it shows that the pressure must decrease as we go upward in the atmosphere—that is, p_2 must always be less than p_1 so that their difference will balance the downward force due to the weight of the air. It also shows that the difference between p_1 and p_2 (for a particular vertical distance) must be greater when the air density is greater (that is, when the air weighs more).

Now we may return to our original statement that we must know the mean molecular weight if we are to find the temperature from measurements of pressure or density. Suppose that the pressure has been measured, say from a rocket, at the two heights z_1 and z_2, and at several heights in between. We can easily calculate the average density between the two heights by using the hydrostatic equation, since the value of g is well known. Then we can use the equation of state with this mean density and a mean value of the measured pressures to calculate a mean temperature—*if* we know the mean molecular weight m.

As a matter of fact, this is the method usually used

for determining temperature in the upper atmosphere, since it is much easier to measure pressure (or density) from a moving rocket than it is to measure the temperature directly. But if the value of m is not known, this method cannot be used. Actually, m does have about the same value as at the ground up to as high as 80 to 90 km. The problems that develop at higher levels will be discussed later in this chapter.

"Trace" Constituents

There are many other reasons besides the one outlined above for needing to know the composition of air very accurately. Certain gases are very important, even if they are present in such small amounts that they do not affect the air's molecular weight appreciably.

One example occurring even near the ground is carbon dioxide, which, as shown in Table 3, makes up only 0.033 per cent of air. There is considerable evidence showing that this gas has become more abundant during the last 100 years, as a result of man's industrial activity. Suppose, for the sake of argument, that this amount should double or triple during the next 100 years. This change would have no noticeable effect on the molecular weight of air, because there is so little carbon dioxide to begin with, but it might be extremely important for other reasons. Carbon dioxide is a very efficient absorber of infrared radiation, and, along with water vapor and clouds, intercepts and returns to earth much of the radiation leaving the ground. This fact causes the surface temperature to be higher than it would be otherwise. If the amount of carbon dioxide were doubled or tripled, the surface temperature would become, on the average, higher. How much higher we are not certain, but some scientists have argued that this change might have a very important effect on world climate.

Ozone

Another important trace constituent is ozone. Ozone is, as mentioned in Chapter 1, the triatomic molecule of oxygen; that is, it consists of three atoms of oxygen bound together in a molecule and is given the chemical symbol O_3. Ozone is present near the ground but only in very small amounts, and is included under "others" in Table 3. In the upper atmosphere, however, ozone becomes really important, though it is still so rare that it does not affect the mean molecular weight of the air at any altitude.

Figure 11 shows a measurement of the ozone density at different altitudes over Tallahassee, Florida, on March 12, 1965. This measurement was made by sending an instrument called an ozone meter, or ozone sonde, up on a balloon. A small pump circulated air through the instrument, and the ozone in the air underwent a chemical reaction with a solid substance called Rhodamine B, which had been placed in the ozone meter. The heat given off by this reaction was detected and measured by a sensitive phototube, which in turn altered a radio signal according to the amount of heat and therefore the amount of ozone. A measurement was made every 15 seconds. With the balloon rising about 300 meters per minute, this allowed for measurement at about every 75 meters, although some of these measurements have been averaged in preparing Figure 11.

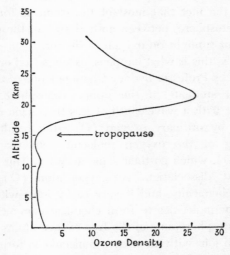

Figure 11. Ozone Distribution over Tallahassee, Florida, on March 12, 1965. Notice that ozone density is markedly greater between 18 km and 31 km than it is at lower altitudes. The ozone density would continue to fall if we had the measurements for higher altitudes.

A large number of such measurements by this and similar methods has been made. There are important differences from time to time and place to place, but all measurements show that the ozone density in the lower stratosphere is greater than at the earth's surface. Usually the greatest ozone density is found between 20 and 30 km above the earth, and there is as a rule a sharp rise in the ozone density starting just above the tropopause.

Why should ozone have this peculiar behavior? Air itself, and the principal gases making up air, have their greatest density near the ground. The answer lies in the fact that most of the ozone is formed in the stratosphere, between 20 and 50 km, through the action of sunlight on oxygen in the air.

Briefly, this is what happens, as suggested originally in 1930 by Professor Sydney Chapman, one of the most eminent students of the upper atmosphere. When sunlight with a wavelength of less than 2400 A is absorbed by ordinary oxygen (O_2), the result is the splitting of the oxygen molecule into two atoms ($O + O$), which go their separate ways. This process is called "dissociation." An oxygen atom (O) is very active chemically, and it very easily joins with other atoms or molecules to form chemical compounds. In the stratosphere, one of the free oxygen atoms is most likely to join with an oxygen molecule to form ozone ($O + O_2 \rightarrow O_3$). Now, ozone itself can be broken up by the action of sunlight ($O_3 + \text{sunlight} \rightarrow O_2 + O$) or by collision with an oxygen atom ($O_3 + O \rightarrow O_2 + O_2$). The net result of all these chemical reactions, which are summarized in Table 4, is that ozone molecules are constantly being formed and destroyed but some are always present.

Ozone is not formed in this way near the ground, or anywhere in the troposphere, because the sunlight that starts the chain, with wavelength less than 2400 A, does not penetrate this deeply into the atmosphere; it is all absorbed in the stratosphere and above. There is ozone in the troposphere, as Figure 11 shows, but most of it arrives there after having been formed at high levels and transported downward by air motions. A small amount is also formed by lightning, when it can sometimes be detected by its characteristic odor.

As discussed in Chapter 3, the absorption of ultra-

TABLE 4
PRODUCTION AND DISSOCIATION OF OZONE

I. *Production of Ozone*

1. $O_2 + \text{sunlight} \rightarrow O + O$

then

2. $O + O_2 \rightarrow O_3$

II. *Dissociation of Ozone*

1. $O_3 + \text{sunlight} \rightarrow O_2 + O$

or

2. $O_3 + O \rightarrow O_2 + O_2$

violet sunlight by ozone is responsible for the temperature rise in the upper stratosphere and the temperature maximum at the stratopause (see Figure 1). So here is a trace constituent that significantly changes the temperature of an entire layer of the atmosphere. Ozone also has potential value in meteorological studies as what is called a "tracer." At low enough elevations (say below 20 km), ozone is hardly affected by the chemical reactions just described. A particular "parcel" of air, or collection of air molecules, maintains its ozone content unchanged for long periods of time, as it moves about. With proper measurements, we could use this fact to help trace the movements of particular air parcels.

Nitric Oxide and Hydroxyl

Two other trace constituents that are particularly important are nitric oxide and hydroxyl. Nitric oxide (NO) is formed in the thermosphere and mesosphere as a result of complex chemical reactions involving both nitrogen and oxygen. The special importance of nitric oxide is in its being quite easily ionized; that is, it can lose one of its electrons more easily than can O_2 or N_2, for example. This question of ionization will be discussed in the next chapter, so it is best to avoid too much detail at this point. We shall see at that time that most of the free electrons between 60 and 80 km, which affect radio transmission in important ways, probably come from this minor gas.

The airglow, which was mentioned in both Chapters 1 and 2, and which will be discussed in greater detail in Chapter 8, has presented many puzzles to scientists. One of these problems had to do with the cause of several bands of closely spaced lines in the visible and near infrared part of the airglow spectrum. The positions of these lines do not correspond to the known emission of any of the abundant atmospheric gases, although some were mistakenly attributed to nitrogen. In 1950, after careful observation of these bands, and comparison with both theory and laboratory measurements, A. B. Meinel suggested the answer to this puzzle. They are given off by hydroxyl (OH), which is formed by chemical reactions in the mesosphere after water vapor is dissociated by sunlight. Thus, a large part of the energy radiated by the upper atmosphere at night is radiated by this rare and minor gas.

Dissociation of Oxygen and Nitrogen

We have already related in our discussion of ozone how oxygen (O_2) can be dissociated. In the stratosphere, where ozone is formed, only a tiny fraction of the molecules is affected, and practically all of the oxygen present remains as O_2. However, the situation is quite different in the thermosphere, where sunlight dissociates most of the oxygen molecules, so that the oxygen is found mostly in its atomic form. This, too, was suggested in 1930 by Professor Chapman.

The dissociation of oxygen has important consequences. Atomic oxygen behaves quite differently from molecular or diatomic oxygen, both in its chemical properties and in its ability to absorb solar radiation. Furthermore, it has a molecular weight of only 16, compared with 32 for O_2. So when air contains an important fraction of its oxygen in atomic form, it has a smaller mean molecular weight. Unfortunately, we do not know the exact proportion of atomic to molecular oxygen at elevations above 90 km, so we do not know the exact molecular weight at a particular elevation. This uncertainty makes the interpretation of pressure, density, and temperature measurements through the equation of state and the hydrostatic equation quite difficult.

At this point, the reader might well wonder how scientists have been able to measure the composition of air at such high elevations. The first idea that might come to mind is that of capturing a sample of air from a rocket, recovering it at the ground, and subjecting the contents to laboratory analysis. This has, indeed, been tried, but it does not work very well because of the difficulty of getting a representative sample of air from a moving rocket. In the particular case of molecular oxygen, some measurements from rockets have been made by observing wavelengths from the sun which are absorbed by O_2. At low enough elevations, not much sunlight is observed in this wavelength region because of oxygen absorption. As the rocket ascends, there is less and less oxygen between it and the sun, so that more and more sunlight of those wavelengths reaches the instrument. By measuring carefully how the solar radiation changes as the rocket moves upward, it is possible to determine how much oxygen there is at each level.

Finally, probably the most useful method is an adaptation of a common laboratory instrument, the mass spectrometer. The molecules from a sample of gas, in this case air, are ionized and move as charged particles in a combined electric and magnetic field in the instrument. Exactly how they move depends on how heavy they are, and from this we can find out the molecular weights and therefore the identities of the various gases in the mixture.

Both radiation measurements and mass-spectrometer measurements have shown that oxygen is mostly atomic, rather than molecular, above 100 to 120 km. The exact ratio of atoms to molecules has appeared to be different according to different measurements. Some of this difference might be due to experimental errors, but it is likely that there are actually changes in the ratio from time to time and place to place, just as the "weather" changes near the earth's surface. On the other hand, the mass-spectrometer measurements have shown that nitrogen remains mostly molecular up to at least 200 km. Some atomic nitrogen is formed, but only a small percentage of the N_2 molecules are dissociated.

Diffusive Equilibrium

In many ways air behaves as if it were a single gas and not a mixture of different kinds of gases. For example, at the beginning of this chapter, we wrote just one equation of state and one hydrostatic equation for air, and we got around the fact that there are several different gases in the air by using a mean molecular weight.

For high elevations in the atmosphere, this simplification will not work. The density of air becomes very, very low, the molecules are on the average quite far apart, and collisions between the molecules become very rare. Finally, when the density is low enough, each gas in the mixture begins to behave as if the other gases were not present at all. Then each gas must be treated separately, with its own equation of state, its own hydrostatic equation, and its own molecular weight. This situation is called *diffusive equilibrium*. In diffusive equilibrium, the lighter gases tend to rise to the top, like the cream in a bottle of milk. We should expect therefore that as we go higher and higher in the thermosphere the composition will change drastically, with the lighter gases becoming more prevalent.

This phenomenon has indeed been observed through the use of mass-spectrometer measurements from rockets and satellites. Diffusive equilibrium begins at about 110 to 120 km. At altitudes of a few hundred kilometers, air consists mostly of atomic oxygen, which is of course lighter than either N_2 or O_2. At still higher elevations, say around 1000 km, the most prominent gas is helium, the molecular weight of which is only 4. Finally, on the fringe of the atmosphere, "air" consists mostly of atomic hydrogen, the lightest gas of all. There is certainly not very much helium or hydrogen at these high elevations; they predominate simply because the more abundant, heavier gases are pulled in closer to the earth in order to maintain a hydrostatic equilibrium.

Some readers might want to look into the question of diffusive equilibrium in a little more detail. Those who have trouble with equations can skip the remainder of this chapter without missing any new ideas.

In diffusive equilibrium, each gas has its own pressure, density, and molecular weight. All are presumed to have the same temperature, although this may not be a very good assumption at very high levels. The hydrostatic equation for one gas can be written

$$p_1 - p_2 = \rho g \, (z_2 - z_1)$$

where the symbols are the same as used in the first part of this chapter (see Figure 10), but now the density and pressures refer to only the one gas. Now we can substitute for the density of this gas from the equation of state for the gas $\rho = mp/RT$ and get the equation

$$\frac{p_1 - p_2}{p} = \frac{mg \, (z_2 - z_1)}{RT}$$

Notice that the molecular weight m appears on the right side of this equation. *The fractional change of pressure is greater for a heavier gas.* This means that in the same vertical distance with the same mean temperature, the pressure of a heavier gas changes more than does the pressure of a lighter gas. Eventually, the pressure of heavier gases, such as N_2 and

O_2, approaches zero, while the pressure of the lighter gases, like atomic oxygen, helium, and hydrogen, have not yet become so small. According to the equation of state, the very low pressures of the heavier gases lead also to very low densities.

It is not that *all* the hydrogen and helium rises to the top of the atmosphere. It is simply that these gases spread out over a greater vertical distance in the gravitational field, so that at high enough altitudes they are all that is left. The rest of the gases have already "faded away."

We have referred frequently in previous chapters to ions and ionization and since these affect extensive regions of the atmosphere it is time to examine them in more detail.

VI

The Ionosphere

The *ionosphere*, as mentioned in Chapter 1, is the part of the atmosphere that contains ions and free electrons in numbers sufficient to affect radio waves. Ions, it should be remembered, are atoms or molecules that have lost one or more electrons and are therefore positively charged. Free electrons are not bound to any atom or molecule and each carries a negative charge. The ionosphere has its lower limit at about 60 km above the earth's surface and extends upward to the outer edge of the atmosphere. You may notice that the ionosphere includes most of the mesosphere and all of the thermosphere, and that it is not a separate region in terms of its altitude limits. Nevertheless, scientists prefer to use the word "ionosphere" when they are talking about effects for which the presence of the electrons and ions is important.

The ordinary atom or molecule is electrically neutral. It contains a certain number of protons, each carrying a definite positive charge of electricity, and the same number of electrons, each carrying an equivalent definite negative charge of electricity. The positive charges on the protons and the negative charges on the electrons exactly cancel one another. If one of the electrons leaves the atom or molecule, carrying with it its negative charge, it leaves behind an atom or molecule with a net positive charge, called an *ion*. This process in which electrons escape is called *ionization*.

In the lower atmosphere, except near thunderstorms, there are very few ions or free electrons. In the ionosphere, although most of the atoms and molecules still remain electrically neutral, there are enough ions and free electrons to be important in many problems. The usual cause of ionization is the absorption of solar radiation of a very short wavelength. Ionization is also caused in special cases by collisions with very high-energy particles which sometimes enter the upper atmosphere from the sun.

The presence of the ionosphere is one of the most practical reasons for studying the upper atmosphere. As you may remember from Chapter 1, the ionosphere affects radio waves reaching it or passing through it, and thus makes possible long-distance radio communication. When you turn on your radio and hear a broadcast from a station more than about 50 miles away, you are hearing radio signals that have been reflected from the ionosphere. If you have a short-wave set, you may hear broadcasts from halfway around the world, because of the existence of the iono-sphere.

Historical Notes

The story of the discovery and exploration of the ionosphere is both interesting and instructive. It illustrates how scientific studies proceed from unex-plained observations, to theories that might explain them, to further observations that test the theories, and so on through repeating cycles of observation and theory.

When Marconi invented the "wireless," there was no real expectation that it could ever be used for com-munication over very long distances. It was known that the radio signals were carried on electromagnetic radiation, similar to light but of much longer wave-length, as was pointed out in Chapter 4, and that elec-tromagnetic radiation ordinarily travels in straight lines. Therefore it was expected that the signal from a transmitter to a receiver would have to follow a "line of sight" path; that is, a straight line unimpeded by hills, trees, houses, or similar obstructions. Because of the curvature of the earth, this would limit reception even if the transmitter were placed on a high tower to distances well under 100 miles.

The scientific world was therefore surprised and hard put for an explanation when as we discussed briefly in Chapter 2 Marconi in 1901 succeeded in re-ceiving the radio signal from Cornwall, England, at

Newfoundland in Canada, a distance of about 2000 miles. We have already mentioned how the American Kennelly, and the Englishman Heaviside both theorized that the earth's upper atmosphere might contain a conducting layer that the radio waves could not penetrate. Actually this was not the first time that the possibility of a conducting layer in the upper atmosphere had been suggested. Some 20 years earlier, writing in the Encyclopaedia Britannica, a British scientist named Balfour Stewart had conjectured that such a layer might exist. He was attempting to explain small changes in the magnetic field near the surface of the earth and felt that these might be due to electric currents flowing in a conducting layer in the upper atmosphere. However, Stewart's idea seemed to have no practical use, and furthermore there was no way at that time to check its accuracy by observations. It consequently went almost unnoticed. We shall discuss magnetic variations and upper-atmosphere currents more closely in Chapter 7.

Now let us return to the developments following the work of Kennelly and Heaviside. Science moved slowly in those days, compared with the rapid pace of the present day. It was 1912 before W. H. Eccles attempted to develop the Kennelly-Heaviside suggestion in mathematical detail, and still 12 years later that J. Larmor made a further theoretical study. Their work forms the basis for the modern-day theory of wave propagation in the ionosphere.

But theory was not enough. What was needed was clear-cut experimental verification of the presence of a reflecting ionosphere. This was provided in 1925 by the British scientists Appleton and Barnett and in 1926 by the Americans Breit and Tuve. We shall de-

scribe the latter experiment shortly, because it became
the basis of most ionospheric observations before the
development of rockets and satellites.

From that point on, knowledge of the ionosphere
has increased rapidly. The theory was fully developed
by 1932, and observations by radio-sounding methods
became routine at a number of observatories. It will
be the purpose of the rest of this chapter to outline
what has been learned from these and succeeding
studies.

Radio-Soundings of the Ionosphere

Suppose a radio transmitter sends a radio signal or "pulse" of very short duration (about 10^{-4} second) upward. A receiver in the vicinity of the transmitter detects this signal several times. The first time,
it receives the signal horizontally over a direct line-of-
sight path, the second time it receives a reflected signal that has traveled up to the ionosphere and back
down, the third time it also receives a reflected signal
that has traveled up, down, up, and down again, and
so forth, as shown in Figure 12. This was the experiment of Breit and Tuve, which was just mentioned.

The length of time that the first reflected signal
takes to travel up to the ionosphere and back down to
the receiver can be accurately measured. If the signal
is at a frequency of about 1 megacycle—or 1,000,000
cycles—per second, abbreviated mc, which is in the
middle of the standard broadcast band, the length of
time for one reflection corresponds to travel up to
about 100 km and back again. If now the frequency
is increased, the length of time increases, indicating

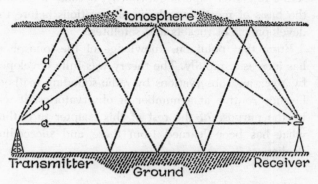

Figure 12. A Diagram Showing the Experiment of Breit
and Tuve. These are the first four signals which
will be received. A is the line-of-sight signal, B
is reflected once by the ionosphere, C twice,
and D three times; the receiver might be much
closer to the transmitter than is shown here.

reflection from a higher level. When the frequency is
greater than 10 to 15 mc no reflected signal is detected. Figure 13 shows a diagram comparing frequency with the time for the pulse to travel up and
back down again. Notice the breaks in the curve at
about 3 to 4 mc and at about 6 to 7 mc. We shall come
back to a discussion of these shortly. The apparatus
used in this experiment is called an *ionosonde*, and
curves like the one shown in Figure 13 are called
ionograms.

The experiment just described has proved to be
very valuable for studies of the ionosphere. Of course,
in the usual radio broadcast, radiation is emitted continuously and not in pulses, and we are interested
in long-distance transmission. Radiation entering the
ionosphere at an angle is bent or refracted downward,

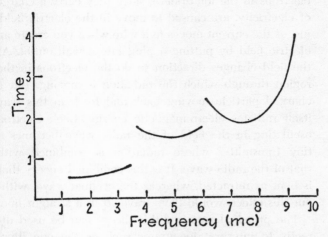

Figure 13. An Ionogram. The time is given in milliseconds (thousandths of a second).

in much the same way as was described in Chapter 2 for sound waves in the upper stratosphere (see Figure 5). But in this case the refraction is caused not by the temperature distribution, but by the distribution of free electrons and, to a much lesser extent, of positive ions.

This behavior is now very well understood but the detailed theory of radio waves traveling through the ionosphere is very complicated. However, the principle is simple enough, and the main result can be described easily. Electromagnetic radiation involves electric and magnetic fields that oscillate back and forth very rapidly[4] as it proceeds outward. The free

---

[4] As a matter of fact the "wavelength" that we have referred to so often is the distance between consecutive points where these fields are in the same direction, and the frequency tells the number of times a second that the field changes direction at

electrons in the ionosphere, since they carry a charge of electricity, are caused to move in the electric field, just as the current moves in a wire when you create an electric field by putting a plug into a wall outlet. As the field changes direction so do the electrons in the region through which the radiation is moving. But a charged particle moving back and forth in this way itself radiates electromagnetic energy. Each electron oscillating in the field of the radio wave becomes a tiny transmitter whose radiation is combined with that of the radio wave. It is this combined energy that is bent or refracted, whereas the original wave, without this effect, would have traveled in a straight line.

The principal result of this theory can be used directly to interpret ionograms such as the one illustrated in Figure 13. It turns out that under most circumstances a pulse carrying radiation of frequency f and traveling straight upward is reflected from a level with a particular electron density N. If f is expressed in cycles per second and N is the number of free electrons found in a cubic centimeter, the relation between them is

$$N = 1.24 \times 10^{-8} f^2$$

Let us make a simple calculation with this equation, just as an example. If the frequency is 2 mc, f equals 2×10^6 cycles per second and f^2 is 4×10^{12}. Then N at the level of reflection must be $1.24 \times 10^{-8} \times 4 \times 10^{12} = 4.96 \times 10^4$. Thus there are 49,600 electrons in a cubic centimeter of air at the level of reflection. Now a

---

a given place. Thus, a frequency of 1 mc means that the electric (or magnetic) field oscillates back and forth 1,000,000 times each second as the radiation passes. The product of frequency and wavelength is the speed with which the radiation travels.

look at the ionogram shows us that as the frequency gets larger, the level from which reflection occurs becomes higher. This means that the electron density must be larger at the higher levels. For example a pulse of frequency 4 mc is reflected from a higher elevation, where N is 19.84×10^4.

But what of the "breaks" in the ionogram curve? Consider Figure 14, where we show N increasing as we go upward, but with a little "bump" or maximum value at about 120 km. Low frequencies are reflected

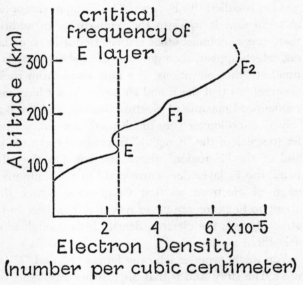

Figure 14. Change of Electron Density with Height. Note the "bump," or maximum value, for the E layer.

from below this maximum, and as the frequency is increased the level of reflection moves up toward it.

The frequency that just corresponds to the electron density at the maximum is called the *critical frequency* of this maximum, or layer. Higher frequencies have to go farther up to be reflected, as is shown in the picture. Consequently, there is a "break" in the ionogram curve.

Many thousands of observations have shown that there are three such layers of the ionosphere that appear quite regularly. The lowest, at about 120 km, is called the E layer; the next at about 150 to 200 km is called the F_1 layer; and the highest, at around 250 to 300 km is called the F_2 layer. The F_1 layer disappears at night and is weak in the wintertime. In addition there are sometimes other critical frequencies, or layers, which appear, then go away after short periods of time, at other elevations. We now know from rocket observations that the E and F_1 layers do not have very pronounced maxima of electron density, and the term "layer" is no longer very much used. Instead, we prefer to speak of the "E region" from about 90 to 160 km and of the "F region" above 160 km. On the other hand, the F_2 layer does correspond to a definite maximum of electrons so that frequencies higher than about 10 to 15 mc are never reflected. Nowhere in the atmosphere is the electron density high enough to reflect these waves.

You might wonder why the letters "E" and "F" are used. The story told is that Sir Edward Appleton, one of the most renowned students of the ionosphere, used the letter "E" in his theoretical studies to designate the electric field of the wave reflected from the lowest of these three layers. When he found that there were reflections from another and higher layer, he chose "F" as a symbol for the electric field of the wave reflected from there. Finally he decided to use these letters as names of the layers, leaving the earlier letters of the alphabet available for the naming of possible undiscovered layers at lower levels. As we shall discuss in the next section, there is indeed a D region below the E region.

The D Region and Absorption

Note that the ionogram in Figure 13 begins at a low frequency of about 1 mc. Occasionally there are weak reflections of lower-frequency waves from lower elevations. These correspond to weak layers in what is called the D region, below 90 km. The electron density in the D region is quite low, and in addition there is another very important effect called *absorption*, which occurs mostly in the D region.

Recall our discussion earlier in this chapter of how electrons oscillate in the electric field of a radio wave. As long as they move back and forth unimpeded no energy is lost. The energy that is taken from the radio wave to set the electrons in motion is regained in the radiation that they give off. But if one of the tiny electrons happens to collide with a much heavier molecule or atom, its energy is lost, both to itself and to the propagating radio wave. If this happens enough times, the radio wave will be seriously weakened or may even disappear. This process is called absorption.

Absorption is not very important in the E and F regions, because the likelihood of collisions is quite small. In the D region, at a lower level of the atmosphere, the overall density is much higher, the electrons and neutral molecules are therefore closer together, and there are many more collisions. Here absorption becomes very important. It turns out also that absorption is a more serious problem for the lower-frequency waves.

Absorption is most extensive during the daytime and becomes very weak at night. This is because the D region contains many more electrons during the day than it does at night. Did you ever notice that your ordinary radio at home often receives stations at night from several hundred miles away, stations that you are never able to hear in the daytime? The reason is simple. In order for such a broadcast to travel several hundred miles, the radio wave must follow a zigzag path between the surface and the reflecting layer, which is in the E region for the standard-band AM broadcasts. Therefore, it must follow a slant path through the D region twice for each reflection—once on the way up and once on the way down. During the day, there is so much absorption in the D region that the signal never reaches your receiver. At night, when there is much less absorption, the stronger signals can get through.

Perhaps you have or know someone who has a short-wave receiver, maybe even a transmitter, in the case of a "ham" radio operator. If so, you know that long-distance communication is possible even during the daytime with this equipment. This is because these radio waves are at a higher frequency and are for that reason usually not seriously affected by absorption.

Sometimes even shortwave radios can be "blacked out" by absorption. This occurs when the electron content of the D region, and to some extent that of the E region, is greatly increased by a solar disturbance. In the case of a strong solar flare, which we discussed in Chapter 4, additional solar radiation reaches the D region and produces the extra electrons through increased ionization over most of the sunlit hemisphere. Such an occurrence is termed a "sudden ionospheric disturbance" (abbreviated SID) or a "shortwave fadeout" (abbreviated SWF).

Fadeouts are particularly frequent and severe in high latitudes, around 60° to 70° North or South. This is because additional electrons are produced by collisions with charged particles coming from the sun during solar disturbances and most of these charged particles enter the upper atmosphere at high latitudes. We shall understand the reason for this when we consider the effects of the earth's magnetic field in Chapter 8.

Formation and Variations of the Ionosphere

Radio-soundings and rocket and satellite measurements have shown that there are very large variations in the characteristics of the ionosphere, from day to night, from season to season, and from sunspot-minimum to sunspot-maximum. In order to understand these variations, we must consider what causes the presence of the ionosphere.

We have already said that, except for special times and places where collisions with solar particles are important, ions and free electrons are produced by the absorption of solar electromagnetic radiation. So we should expect that there will be more of these when the sun is directly overhead, less when the sun is near the horizon and shining at an angle, and still less at night when the sun is absent. We might also expect that if there is more solar radiation during the years

of sunspot-maximum, there will thus also be more electrons and ions during those years.

These expectations are generally fulfilled. But there
are other factors to take into account. An electron torn
away from an atom or molecule by radiation from the
sun eventually joins a positive ion to form a neutral
molecule or atom. This process by which electrons and
positive ions "disappear" is called *recombination*. It
is not as simple and straightforward a process as you
might think. Just as energy was needed (from the
solar radiation) to separate the ion and electron in
the first place, so the same amount of energy is re-
leased or made available when they rejoin. The new
neutral molecule must find some way to dispose of
this energy, or the union will be highly temporary and
the electron will again go on its separate way. Exactly
how this recombination is accomplished, in different
ways in different parts of the ionosphere, is complex
and not appropriate for discussion in this book. We do
need to remember, though, that, whatever the details,
recombination is faster when the density is higher,
there then being a better chance for collisions to occur
and for the necessary chemical reactions to take place.
The number of electrons present at any time and
place represents a sort of balance between the rate at
which they are produced by the sun and the rate at
which they disappear through recombination. The
faster the rate of production and the slower the rate
of recombination, the greater the number of electrons
will be.

In the D region, the production of electrons is very
slow, because the solar radiation that can ionize O_2
and N_2 has already been absorbed at higher elevations. As a matter of fact, there is still some question

as to why there are any free electrons at all in this region. Solar radiation in the Lyman alpha line can penetrate this far, but it cannot ionize O_2 or N_2. The Belgian aeronomer, Marcel Nicolet, pointed out in 1945 that the Lyman alpha radiation can ionize nitric oxide, believed to be a trace constituent of the mesosphere. Nicolet's hypothesis is commonly accepted, because there seems to be no other explanation.

It is also true that in the D region recombination is rapid because density and collision frequency are high. Slow production and rapid recombination mean that there are usually not many electrons in the D region. At night when the sun is absent, these electrons disappear almost completely.

After a solar flare appears, the sun gives off hard X-ray radiation (wavelength less than 6 A), which is usually almost totally absent. This kind of radiation can reach the D region and can ionize any of the molecules. This accounts for the greater electron density, resulting in the radio fadeouts which follow solar flares.

At higher elevations in the ionosphere, we find that production increases and recombination decreases so that, as already noted, there are more electrons at the higher elevations. The number of electrons in the E region follows the sun quite closely, with the greatest numbers around noon, in the summer, in sunspot-maximum years. Many of the electrons disappear at night, but recombination is slower than in the D region and a significant number survive the night. There is not enough time for them all to recombine before the sun begins its production again at sunrise.

The greatest production rate at any elevation is believed to occur in the lower F region, probably in the vicinity of the F_1 layer around 160 to 200 km. However, the greatest electron density is found much higher, at the F_2 layer, about 250 to 300 km, because recombination is slower at the higher level and the electrons that are produced last, on the average, much longer. The F_2 layer behaves strangely in many respects. In fact, it has been called the "rogue layer" by Sir Edward Appleton. For example, the F_2 critical frequency, which you will remember depends on the maximum electron density in the F_2 region, is often greater in late afternoon than at noontime, and it sometimes even increases during the night when the sun is absent. Partly these "anomalies," as they are called, are due to the slow recombination rate, but some of them are the result of vertical movements of the electrons. That is, electrons formed at one level may move to another before recombination takes place. The exact nature of these movements is not yet known in detail.

Reflection of Radio Waves

Let us now look more closely at the problem of the reflection of radio waves by the ionosphere when the beam enters the ionosphere at an angle. To be completely accurate, we would have to introduce some very involved mathematics and some new physical ideas, such as the effect of the earth's magnetic field on the bending of the radio wave. But this is not really necessary for understanding what is going on and, as a matter of fact, the ideas we shall use are very nearly correct under most circumstances.

We do, though, have to make use of one equation and of some trigonometry. If you are not yet familiar with trigonometry or have forgotten it, you should still be able to follow the argument by reading carefully.

Suppose that a radio wave of frequency f (expressed in cycles per second) enters the ionosphere at an angle A with the vertical, as shown in Figure 15. As it passes through the ionosphere, it will be bent toward the horizontal and, if f is small enough, it will finally turn and move toward the ground, as the figure shows. The equation we must use lets us calculate

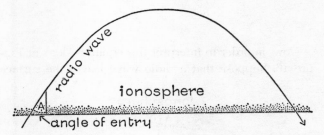

Figure 15. The Refraction of a Radio Wave in the Ionosphere.

whether or not this will happen. It says that

$$f = 0.898 \times 10^4 \, (\sec A) \, \sqrt{N}$$

and will need a little explanation. In the first place, "sec A" is an abbreviation for "secant of the angle A" and will be quite familiar to you if you have studied trigonometry. If you have not, you can look in Table 5, which gives some values of sec A for different angles A. N is the electron density, expressed in number of electrons per cubic centimeter.

TABLE 5
VALUES OF SOME SECANTS

A	Secant A
0°	1.00
10°	1.02
20°	1.06
30°	1.15
40°	1.31
50°	1.56
60°	2.00
70°	2.92
80°	5.76

Now, in order to interpret this equation, look at Figure 16. Suppose that a radio wave leaves the surface

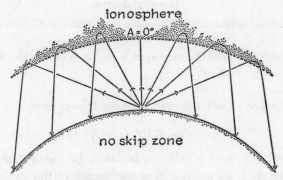

Figure 16. Radio Wave Propagation with no Skip Zone. The wave for which A = 0° returns to the ground.

of the earth traveling in all directions. The portion of it traveling straight up has A = 0° and, according to the table, sec A = 1 when A = 0°. This portion is reflected directly back down from the level where N = 1.24 × 10^{-8} f^2, which is exactly the same as the equation we used earlier in this chapter when we discussed vertical pulses. But now consider a portion of the radio wave that enters the ionosphere at another angle. Take A = 30°, for example. According to the table, sec A = 1.15 for A = 30°. Since sec A is larger than in the previous example, $\sqrt{N}$ must be smaller if their product is to give the same f. Therefore this wave will be reflected at a level where N is smaller than 1.24 × 10^{-8} f^2, that is, at a lower elevation in the ionosphere. Notice also that it does not come back to the original location but is bent gradually so it may travel a long distance away from the transmitter. Such a wave might be reflected by the earth's surface and returned to the ionosphere to be reflected again and thus reach even greater distances.

To follow this problem a little more, suppose that we are dealing with a rather high frequency and that there is nowhere in the ionosphere a value of N large enough to cause reflection of the *vertical* wave. For example, f might be 12 mc, in which case f^2 is 144 × 10^{12} (remember that we must put f in cycles per second to use our equation) and therefore requires an N of 1.79 × 10^6 electrons per cubic centimeter for reflection of the vertical wave to be possible. If the biggest N above the transmitter is less than this, say 1.50 × 10^6, then there will be no reflection, and this portion of the radio wave will travel right through the ionosphere into outer space. But this is not so for portions of the wave entering the ionosphere at large angles. When A is greater than 0°, sec A is greater than 1, and N can be smaller. For the example discussed in this paragraph, the portion of the wave with sec A equal to or greater than 1.09, that is with A greater than or equal to about 23°, will be reflected. Can you verify this calculation? Can you repeat it for the case where the biggest N is only 1.21×10^6? These ideas are illustrated in Figure 17.

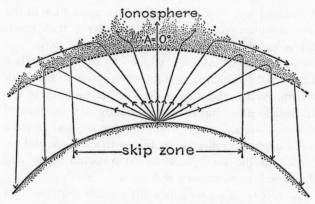

Figure 17. Skip Zone for Radio Waves. Here the frequency of the waves is higher than in Figure 16. Waves must enter the ionosphere at a larger angle in order to be refracted back to earth.

Notice in Figure 17 that there is a region near the transmitter where no reflected energy will be returned to the ground. A receiver in this region, if it is too far away to hear the direct line-of-sight signal, will receive nothing, even though receivers that are farther away may have good reception from the reflected signals. This region is known as a *skip zone;* and it is exactly the same sort of thing as the "zone of silence" for sound waves that we talked about in Chapter 2.

For many summers, our family has spent some time

on Cape Cod, about 60 miles from Boston and about 200 miles from New York. At night we get much better reception on the standard broadcast band from New York stations than from Boston stations. This is because direct reception from Boston is not very good at that distance, and we are in the skip zone for Boston stations. On the other hand, we are at a favorable distance for receiving the reflected signal from certain New York stations. Perhaps you have had a similar experience.

One last point needs to be made, one that was touched upon in the part of this chapter dealing with the D region and with absorption. The careful reader might look at our equation and at Table 5 and decide that even very, very high frequencies can be reflected if the angle A is large enough. And he would be correct as far as this equation is concerned. But notice that as A becomes larger, the path the radio wave must follow through the ionosphere also becomes larger. All the while, it is undergoing absorption in the D and lower E regions. So for very long paths, even at night when the electron density is small, absorption eventually weakens the signal to the point where it cannot be detected. This places an upper limit on usable frequencies that can take advantage of ionospheric reflection. For example, FM and television signals are not ordinarily detected beyond line-of-sight transmission paths, because their frequencies are simply too high.

So much for our brief examination of the ionosphere and some of the experiments we use to measure its properties. Let us now turn to some more phenomena of the upper atmosphere.

VII

Atmospheric Tides
and the Earth's Magnetic Field

We have found it necessary to use the concept of pressure in the atmosphere in order to discuss other properties, but now we should look at it in more detail. One way to measure pressure is with a barometer. Many of you have one in your home or school. A barograph is a barometer that makes a continuous record of the pressure on graph paper which is attached to a rotating drum. Figure 18 shows a typical barograph "trace," or record of pressure over a period of time, for a station near the equator. Notice that the pressure rises and falls more or less regularly twice a day, reaching its highest values between 9 and 10 A.M. and 9 and 10 P.M. The difference between the highest and lowest pressure is about 2 to 3 millibars[5] (abbreviated mb).

This twice-a-day rise and fall of the surface pressure is clearly evident each day at all low-latitude stations, except occasionally when a severe tropical disturbance passes near the station and causes pressure changes that obscure the pattern. This cycle is caused by tides in the atmosphere, which are similar in some

[5] The millibar is the pressure unit most often used by meteorologists. The average sea-level pressure is about 1013 mb, which is equivalent to 29.92 inches of mercury or 760 millimeters of mercury.

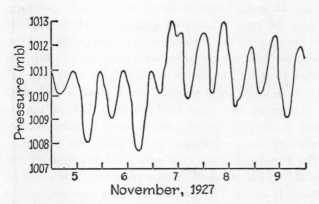

Figure 18. Barograph Trace at Batavia (now Djakarta, 6°S).

ways to the more familiar tides in the ocean. The effects of atmospheric tides are very small near the earth's surface, and it is not surprising if you have never heard of them. But in the upper atmosphere these tides are very important. For example, over England at 80 to 100 km the wind speed may change by as much as 50 meters per second in 6 hours, because of the tides. In this chapter, we shall consider some of the observed features, causes, and effects of atmospheric tides.

Observed Tides near the Surface

Notice that we speak of tides in the plural sense. This is because we have found more than one type of tide in the atmosphere. The largest, which shows up most clearly in Figure 18, has exactly 12 hours between the times of highest pressure, and ex-

actly 12 hours between the times of lowest pressure.
Since this type of tide goes through 1 cycle in one-half
of an ordinary day, as measured by the position of the
sun, we call this the *solar semi-diurnal tide*. We can
refer to it for simplicity as S_2, "S" for solar and "2"
because there are 2 maxima and 2 minima each day.

There are two other kinds of tides that are important in the atmosphere. One of these is called S_1, because it has 1 maximum and 1 minimum each day.
The barograph trace in Figure 18 shows some effects
of S_1, which we shall discuss presently. The other of
these is called L_2, because it has 2 maxima and 2
minima each *lunar* day, that is, during the time it takes
for the *moon* to return to the same apparent position
in the sky (see Figure 21 later in this chapter).

Studies of the Solar Tides

Suppose we wish to study the solar tides at a
station *not* near the equator. If we look at a barograph
trace for one day, the chances are we will not see any
sign of them. Instead the trace will probably show
rather large pressure changes due to traveling pressure systems, the highs and lows that come and go and
affect our weather. In order to find and study S_1 and
S_2 we have to *average* the pressure for each hour over
many, many days. The idea behind this method is that
the highs and lows have no preferred hour to pass our
particular station. At a certain hour, say 10 A.M., we
may have a high on one day, a low on the next day,
and perhaps something in between the two on the
third day. If we average the 10 A.M. pressures for
enough days, these effects, even though large, will

cancel out. On the other hand the tides, even though they are small, always have the *same* pressure effect at 10 A.M., and this effect will still be there after the averaging is done.

Suppose now that after all this averaging is done we know how the surface pressure changes with time because of the solar tides. If the station is near 30°N, the curve will look like the one shown in Figure 19. Note that there are 2 pressure maxima and 2 pressure minima. But notice also that the pressure at the afternoon minimum is lower than at the early morning minimum, and the pressure at the 10 A.M. maximum is somewhat higher than at the evening maximum. Furthermore,

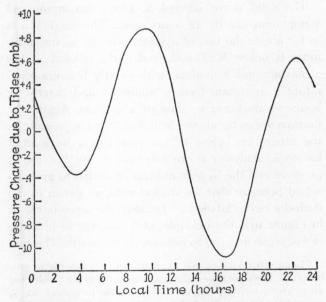

Figure 19. The Effect of Solar Tides on Surface Pressure at 30°N.

the 2 maxima (or minima) are separated by a little more than 12 hours. This means that we are looking at the effect of both S_1 and S_2, one with a 24-hour period and one with a 12-hour period, which add together to give the curve in Figure 19. We should like to separate these and study each one alone.

The procedure for doing this separation is well known to scientists and mathematicians and is called *harmonic analysis*. It is not possible to explain harmonic analysis in detail without much more use of trigonometry and calculus than is desirable in a book of this sort. However, the purpose and result of the analysis should become quite clear to you if you will consider Figure 20.

The solid curve labeled S_1 has 1 maximum and 1 minimum exactly 12 hours apart. The maximum is as far above the line of average pressure as the minimum is below it. The dashed curve labeled S_2 has 2 maxima and 2 minima, with exactly 6 hours separating a maximum from a minimum and exactly 12 hours separating 2 maxima or 2 minima. Again, the maxima are as far above the line of average pressure as the minima are below it. Now (and this is the point of harmonic analysis) at any one time of the day, the S_1 pressure and the S_2 pressure can be added to give the actual pressure that we started with, as shown in the dash-dot curve labeled S^6 (exactly the same curve as in Figure 19). For example, at 6 A.M., the S_1 pressure is +0.38 mb and the S_2 pressure is −0.28 mb. The sum

---

[6] In an actual case S_1 and S_2 might not add together to give *exactly* S. If we continued the harmonic analysis we would find an S_3 curve (with 3 maxima and 3 minima in a day), an S_4 curve, etc. Adding all of these together would give a closer approximation to S. In the atmospheric tides, however, all except S_1 and S_2 are extremely small.

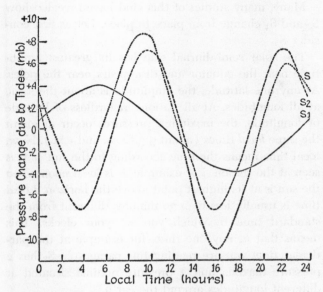

Figure 20. Harmonic Analysis of Solar Tides at 30°N. The curve S shows the combined effect of the S_1 and S_2 curves. This curve is the same as the one in Figure 19.

is +0.10 mb, which was the observed tidal effect at 6 A.M. after the averaging was done.

The curve S of the combined solar tides resembles S_2 more than it does S_1. This is because the S_2 curve has larger amplitude (one-half the difference between maximum and minimum is called the amplitude) than S_1. By studying Figure 20, you can now see why the S curve shows a lower pressure in the afternoon than in the early morning. In the afternoon, both S_1 and S_2 are below average. The difference between the two maxima can be explained in a similar way.

Many, many studies of this kind have revealed how S_2 and S_1 change from place to place. Let us first consider S_2.

The solar semi-diurnal tide has its greatest amplitude near the equator and disappears near the poles. At any one latitude, the amplitude is about the same at all longitudes. At all stations, regardless of latitude or longitude, the maximum pressures occur at about the same *local* times (about 9:30 A.M. and P.M.). Now, local time means the time according to the sun as it is seen at the station. For example, it is local noon when the sun is at its highest point above the horizon. Local time is usually less than 30 minutes different from the standard time by which you set your clocks. This means that at any one time, for example at the particular time you are reading this paragraph, S_2 has 2 pressure maxima and 2 pressure minima situated at different longitudes around the earth.

Let us take an example. Suppose you are in the central United States near longitude 90°W, and the time is about 9:30 A.M. The S_2 pressure is at a maximum at your station. However at Greenwich, England, at this same moment the local time is 3:30 P.M. and the S_2 pressure is at a minimum. In Asia, near 90°E, the local time is 9:30 P.M. and the pressure is at a maximum. The other pressure minimum is located at 180° longitude over the Pacific Ocean. Another way to look at this cycle is that the double-wave of pressure travels from east to west following the apparent motion of the sun.

The solar diurnal (or "daily") tide, S_1, has a smaller amplitude on the average than does S_2, and it does not behave as regularly. The local time of maximum (or minimum) changes from place to place, as does the amplitude. It appears that S_2 is a regular pulsation of the entire atmosphere while S_1 depends much more on local conditions, such as proximity to mountains or oceans.

At this point, the thoughtful reader who knows something about tides in the ocean may well be puzzled. As the ocean tides rise and fall, the *average* time between high tides is about 12 hours and 25 minutes (there are large local variations due to the contours of beaches and harbors). This is one-half of a *lunar* day. You can see why a lunar day is different from a solar day if you study Figure 21. During a solar day

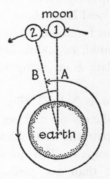

Figure 21. The Lunar Day. While the earth is rotating, the moon is also revolving around it, in the same direction. In order to "catch up" with the moon (moving from position 1 to position 2), the earth must rotate for more than 1 full rotation. This additional rotation (from A to B) requires 50 minutes. Thus, the lunar day is 24 hours 50 minutes long.

of 24 hours, the earth rotates on its axis so that the same point on earth faces the sun once again. But in the meantime, the moon has moved in its orbit around the earth in the direction of the earth's rotation, so that the earth has to rotate for an additional 50 minutes in order to "catch up" with the moon. Tides in the ocean are caused mainly by the gravitational attraction of the moon and thus follow lunar time.

What then about the lunar tide in the atmosphere, with "high tide" or pressure maxima separated by 12 hours and 25 minutes? We have already mentioned that there is one and that it is termed L_2. However, L_2 is so small that even near the equator, where it is largest, there is no sign of it in a single day's barograph trace. It can be found by averaging the surface pressures at particular local *lunar* times, but even near the equator observations for about a year have to be used before it can be found. In middle latitudes, where L_2 is even smaller, data from many tens of years are needed.

The next question is "why?" Why is the lunar tide so much larger in the oceans and yet so much smaller in the atmosphere than the solar tides? If you wonder, you are in good company. This question has puzzled scientists for more than 200 years, including such giants of the scientific world as Laplace and Lord Kelvin. We now know most of the answers, but there are some puzzling aspects yet to be explained.

Causes of the Tides

We have said that the tide in the ocean is caused mainly by the gravitational attraction of the moon. Let us now look into this effect in a little more detail and see how it works.

Any two objects in the universe attract each other with a force called gravity. According to the famous law of Sir Isaac Newton, the equation for this force is

$$F = G \frac{M_1 \, M_2}{r^2}$$

where F is the force, G is a constant of nature, M_1 is the mass of the first object, M_2 is the mass of the second object, and r is the distance between the two objects.

For example, the earth and the moon exert this force on one another. The effect of the force on the moon is to make it travel in a curved orbit around the earth. Were it not for gravity, the moon would travel in a straight line and fly off tangentially into space. The gravitational force of the earth makes it move in a *curved* path and continue to circle the earth, as shown in Figure 22. This same effect causes artificial satellites to circle the earth, and it also makes the earth and the other planets circle the sun.

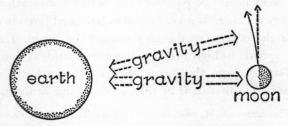

Figure 22. The Revolution of the Moon. The moon (or any object) would travel in a straight line if there were no force acting on it. But the gravitational force between the earth and the moon pulls it into a curved orbit.

But what about the effect of the moon's gravitational force on the earth? The effect is exactly the same, but very much smaller, because the earth is so much more massive than the moon. That is, as a result of the moon's attraction, the earth travels in a relatively small curved orbit[7] in just such a way as to balance that attraction. The chances are good that you have never heard of this motion of the earth. It is separate from the earth's rotation on its axis and its revolution around the sun, and it is usually not mentioned in elementary astronomy texts.

To see how the moon's gravitation causes the ocean tides, consider Figure 23. At the center of the earth, the effect of the earth's small curved orbit exactly balances the attraction of the moon. At point A, nearest the moon, the orbital effect is the same as at the center of the earth, because the earth moves in its orbit as a solid body, but the moon's gravitational force is *greater*. This is because point A is slightly closer to the moon than is the center of the earth, and the r in the denominator of Newton's law is therefore smaller. As a result there is a very small unbalanced force that pulls the ocean (or the air) toward the moon. This corresponds to high tide. On the other hand, at point B, farthest from the moon, the moon's gravitational force is *less* than it is at the center of the earth and

[7] The center of this orbit is about 3000 miles from the center of the earth, at a point called the "center of mass" of the earth-moon system. The position of this center of mass is such that the distance from the center of the earth to the center of mass, multiplied by the earth's mass, is equal to the distance from the center of the moon to the center of mass, multiplied by the moon's mass. Actually, this center of mass is also the point about which the moon revolves.

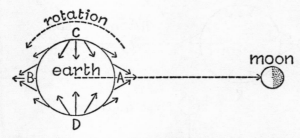

Figure 23. The Ocean Tides. This is a top view of the earth. Tides are high at A, nearest to the moon, where the attraction of the moon is greater than the effect of the earth's small orbit. At B, farthest from the moon, where the effect of the moon's gravitation is less than the orbital effect, tides are also high. Tides are low at C and D. As the earth rotates, the locations of the high and low tides change.

there is a very small unbalanced force away from the moon. This too corresponds to high tide. At point C, and at a corresponding point D on the other side of the earth, low tide occurs. As the earth rotates on its axis, the points A and B that are nearest to or farthest from the moon occur at different longitudes. So at any one place there are 2 high tides and 2 low tides in 1 lunar day.

The sun has the same effect, but only about one-half as strong because its distance from the earth is so much greater than the moon's. Nevertheless, at new moon and full moon, when the earth, moon, and sun are lined up and the gravitational effects add together, the ocean tides are greater than at the moon's first quarter and last quarter. See Figure 24.

This gravitational effect satisfactorily explains the

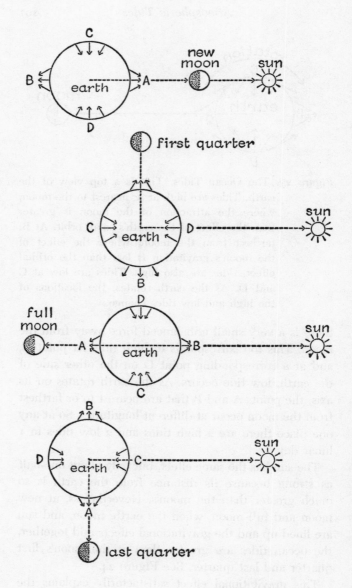

ocean tides, but not the tides in the atmosphere. We have seen that the principal atmospheric tide has a high tide twice in a *solar* day, so there must be something much more complicated going on. As far back as the early 1800s the great French mathematician Laplace realized this and concluded that the atmospheric tides must be due mostly to solar *heating* of the atmosphere, and not to the solar gravitational effect. But if that is so, why are there *two* high tides in the atmosphere each day rather than one? Lord Kelvin summed up this dilemma very well in his presidential address to the Royal Society of Edinburgh in 1882:

The cause of the semi-diurnal variation of barometric pressure cannot be the gravitational tide-generating influence of the sun, because if it were there would be a much larger lunar influence of the same kind, while in reality the lunar barometric tide is insensible, or nearly so. It seems, therefore, certain that the semi-diurnal variation of the barometer is due to temperature. Now the *diurnal* term, in the harmonic analysis of the variation of *temperature*, is undoubtedly much larger in all, or nearly all, places than the *semi-diurnal*. It is then very remarkable that the *semi-diurnal term of the barometric effect* of the variation

---

Figure 24. The Sun's Effect on Ocean Tides. At new moon and full moon, the earth, moon, and sun are in line. The attraction of the sun is added to that of the moon, and high tides are at their highest. At first quarter and last quarter, when the sun and moon are not in line, the tides are not as great.

of temperature should be greater, and so much greater as it is, than the diurnal.

Now you can begin to see why the atmospheric tides, however small they may be near the surface, have interested so many of our finest scientists. They have raised questions that have no easy, obvious answers, a challenge that attracts the true scientist.

I wish we had the time and space to trace out the interesting developments of tidal theory since 1882. However, this would involve some difficult physical ideas that would have to be explained, and this chapter is already getting rather long without yet even reaching the upper atmosphere. We shall simply have to say that Kelvin's idea has turned out to be basically correct. Heating by the sun's rays *is* the main cause of the atmospheric tides, and it has mainly a 24-hour period; that is, it has 1 maximum and 1 minimum during each 24-hour day. It is largest in the day and absent at night. But, just as in the case of the curves shown in Figures 19 and 20, a harmonic analysis can be used to show how the actual curve is made up of 2 ideal curves, one (which we might call H_1) with 1 maximum and 1 minimum every 24 hours, and the other (which we might call H_2) with 2 maxima and 2 minima every 24 hours. The first causes S_1 and the second causes S_2.

As you might suspect, because of the 24-hour period, H_1 is *larger* than H_2. Why then is S_1 *smaller* than S_2? Lord Kelvin suggested an answer for this, too. He said, in the same speech quoted above:

"The explanation probably is to be found by considering the oscillations of the atmosphere, as a whole, in the light of the very formulas which Laplace gave in his *Mécanique céleste* for the ocean, and which he showed to be also applicable to the atmosphere. When thermal influence is substituted for gravitational, in the tide-generating force reckoned for, and when the modes of oscillation corresponding respectively to the diurnal and semi-diurnal terms of the thermal influence are investigated, it will probably be found that the period of free oscillation of the former agrees much less nearly with 24 hours than does that of the latter with 12 hours; and that, therefore, with comparatively small magnitude of the tide-generating force, the resulting tide is greater in the semi-diurnal term than in the diurnal."

This mathematical explanation means simply that the earth's atmosphere *wants* to oscillate with a period of 12 hours much more than it wants to oscillate with a period of 24 hours. A small push every 12 hours has a bigger effect than a larger push every 24 hours. All physical systems have a preferred period (or periods) of oscillation. A simple example is a swing, whose preferred period depends on the length of the rope or chain. You take advantage of this when you push somebody on the swing, by timing your push just right. You push down just when the swing is at its highest point, when your push will do the most good. The period or length of time between pushes is approximately the same whether the swing is moving in a small or a large arc. Time it some time, and then try changing the length of time between your pushes.

You will see, in a very simple case, why sometimes a small force timed just right has more effect than a larger force that is wrongly timed.

In a much more complicated way (which we do not yet understand completely) this is the sort of thing that happens in the atmosphere and causes the semi-diurnal solar tide to be larger than the diurnal solar tide.

Magnetic Changes and the Tides

A magnet, suspended so that it is free to turn in any direction, will turn so that its north pole points approximately northward. This fact has been known for hundreds of years, and is the basis of the magnetic compass. It is the result of the earth's magnetic field, which has its main causes deep inside the earth. To a casual observer, using a compass perhaps for navigational purposes, the earth's magnetic field is very steady and dependable, changing only very gradually over the years.

However, careful and detailed measurements which are carried out at a number of magnetic observatories show that there are very small changes during each day. On some days, these changes are quite regular. That is, the local times when the magnetic field is strongest or weakest are the same from one day to the next and are the same for all stations at the same latitude. These are called "magnetically quiet" days. On other days the changes are larger and unpredictable. These are "magnetically disturbed" days.

Figure 25 shows the typical change of magnetic intensity on a quiet day at about 40°N. "Magnetic intensity" measures the force that is exerted on a magnet. This force might be exerted in any direction, so Figure 25 shows it broken up into three components, a force toward the north, a force toward the east, and a force downward. The biggest change at this latitude

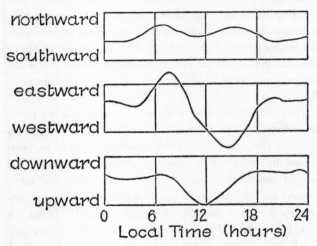

Figure 25. Average Change of Magnetic Intensity on a Quiet Day at 40°N. The change of intensity throughout the day in each of the three components of the magnetic field is shown.

is in the east-west force, which points toward east (positive values) during the night and toward west (negative values) during most of the day. It is important to remember that this change is very small, perhaps 1 part in 5000, or 0.02 per cent, of the intensity of the main field. Without very careful and accurate measurements, a compass needle would still seem to point in the same direction for the whole 24 hours, but the careful measurements show a very small, almost imperceptible swing toward east at night and toward west during the day.

These facts were known in the eighteenth century, but they were not understood. The clue to their explanation came from still another puzzling discovery. After many years of observations, it was found that the amplitude, or amount of change, on the quiet days is larger in sunspot-maximum years than in sunspot-minimum years! This showed that the cause of these changes could not be inside the earth where the main field arises, because sunspots would have no influence there.

These observations led Balfour Stewart, as we mentioned earlier in Chapter 6, to suggest that the causes were in the earth's upper atmosphere. His idea, contained in an article written in 1882 for the Encyclopaedia Britannica, was that the small changes were caused by electric currents flowing in the upper atmosphere, since currents do cause magnetic fields. In fact, he suggested that the upper atmosphere was acting like a dynamo, and his theory came to be called the "dynamo theory."

A dynamo machine (see Figure 26) in its simplest form generates a direct electric current by moving a conductor through a magnetic field. If the ring shown in Figure 26 is caused to rotate in a clockwise direction, current will flow through the wire wound around the ring, as shown by the arrows. This current can be sent through an external circuit by means of the brushes marked "+" and "−."

But what does this have to do with the upper atmosphere? Stewart's idea was that motions of the air, which we think of as "wind," take the place of the ring and move through the earth's main magnetic field.

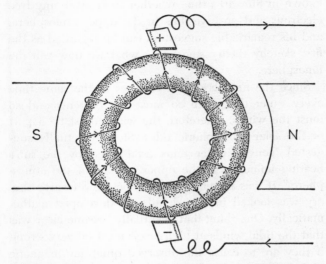

Figure 26. A Dynamo Machine. A magnetic field is generated by the opposite poles (south and north) of the two magnets. When the ring is turned in a clockwise direction, current is induced in the coil. The current flows upward on both sides, as shown by the arrows. The brushes marked "+" and "−" connect this current to an external circuit.

This causes an electric field, just as in the wire, which makes free electrons with a negative charge move in one direction and ions with a positive charge in the other. The motion of the electrons and ions in opposite directions makes up an electric current, which in turn causes the small changes in the magnetic field we observe at the earth's surface. When the wind changes direction, the current also changes direction, and so does the small magnetic field that it causes. It was not known in Stewart's time whether there were any free electrons and positive ions in the upper atmosphere, and his remarkable suggestion can be regarded as the first sketchy theory suggesting what we now call the ionosphere.

Since the magnetic field changes at the same time every quiet day, then so must the currents and so must the winds. Therefore the winds must be a part of the solar atmospheric tides. Stewart actually suggested "convective currents established by the sun's heating influence in the upper regions of the atmosphere." It was many years later before Stewart's theory was looked into in detail and developed mathematically. One thing that eventually became clear was that the tidal winds at high levels must be very strong if they are to cause the observed quiet-day magnetic variations. In the earlier part of this chapter we talked about the tidal effects on surface pressure. There are also tidal winds, which go along with these effects, but at the surface they are extremely small; perhaps a change of 1 cm/sec in wind speed every six hours. But at high levels, the changes must be very large. Only during the last 10 years have measurements shown that this is true. The tidal winds are indeed large at an altitude of 100 km, a few thousand times larger than at the surface, and we shall talk about these measurements shortly.

It is interesting that so many different kinds of research which were apparently unrelated could be tied together in this way. There were scientists who studied the small and apparently unimportant atmospheric tides, other scientists who carefully measured the tiny magnetic variations, others who learned about the relation between electric currents and magnetic fields,

Plate V

Aurora in the form of a homogeneous arc without rays.
(Courtesy of the National Geographic Society — Cornell
University Study of the Aurora.)

Plate VI
Aurora in the form of a rayed arc. (Courtesy of the National Geographic Society — Cornell University Study of the Aurora.)

Plate VII
Aurora in the form of long rays with a band structure.
(Courtesy of the National Geographic Society — Cornell
University Study of the Aurora.)

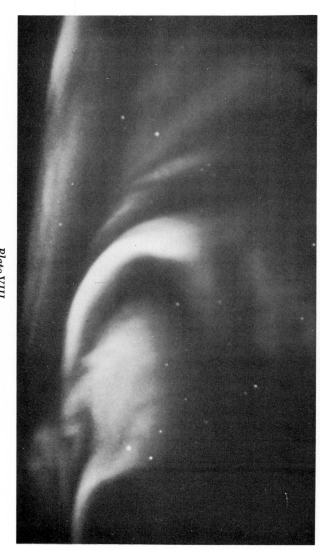

Plate VIII
Aurora taken at the South Pole. (Courtesy of the National Geographic Society — Cornell University Study of the Aurora.)

and still others who counted and kept track of sunspots. None of these men in the nineteenth century could possibly have dreamed that his work taken together with the others' would have anything to do with an ionosphere or with winds 100 km above the earth's surface.

Winds at 80 to 100 km

We saw in Chapter 3 how parachutes and chaff dropped from small rockets can be tracked by radar to measure winds up to 50 to 60 km. This method fails at higher levels, because parachutes and chaff fall too rapidly in the very thin air. We also found that winds could be determined from the rocket-grenade method up to about 80 km, but not higher, because the sound waves from explosions at higher levels cannot be detected at the ground. Above 80 km, other methods must be used.

One of these is sending up a rocket and causing it to release a trail of sodium gas. If this is done at twilight, just before sunrise or after sunset, the sun will shine on the gas in the upper atmosphere, while the ground is in the shadow, as shown in Figure 27. Under these conditions the sodium trail can be seen and photographed from the ground. The trail is blown along by the wind, and a series of photographs can be used to find out how the trail moves and thus what the speed and direction of the wind are. This method is quite expensive and can only be used at twilight, so it is not very useful for the study of tidal winds, which require many observations at all hours of the day.

The other method is to "watch for" meteor trails with radar. Thousands upon thousands of tiny meteors

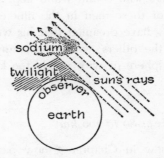

Figure 27. The Sodium-Trail Method of Observing
Winds.

enter the upper atmosphere each day. Only a few of
the largest ones can be seen by eye at night as "shooting stars." But the others leave their trails, because
they ionize the thin column of air through which they
pass. The free electrons and positive ions in the trail
left by the meteor will reflect a radio signal of the
right frequency (about 30 mc). From a study of these
reflected signals, it is possible to tell the direction and
speed of the wind that is blowing the ionized trail
through the atmosphere.

This method of wind observation is called the
"radio-meteor" method and is very useful, because it
can be employed at all hours of the day and night
with ground equipment only. The radio equipment at
Jodrell Bank Observatory in England was used to
measure an average wind for every hour of every day
for several years. On some days, when meteor trails
were especially frequent, an average wind was determined every 20 minutes. On the other hand, the radio-
meteor method gives winds only between about 80
and 105 km—below 80 km there are not enough meteor

trails, and above 105 km they do not last long enough to be observed.

Measurements of this type at Jodrell Bank, at Adelaide in Australia, and a few at Mawson in Antarctica have been used to study the tides. By way of illustration, Figure 28 shows how the average wind between 80 and 105 km changed over Jodrell Bank from noon on September 16 to noon on September 17 in 1954.

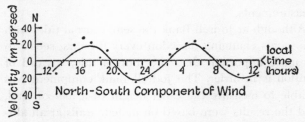

Figure 28. The North-South Wind Component over Jodrell Bank, England, from Noon of September 16 to Noon of September 17, 1954. The solid curve is the result of harmonic analysis. Each dot is an observation.

This figure shows the wind component blowing from south to north, and each dot is the average of the wind speed in this direction for an hour. Notice what large changes there were during this one 24-hour period. At about 4 P.M. the wind was blowing toward the north with a speed around 20 meters per second, but 6 hours later at about 10 P.M. it was blowing toward the south with approximately the same speed. Then in another 6 hours, around 4 A.M., it was blowing toward the north once more.

It is easy to see from this curve and from many others like it that the semi-diurnal solar tide is very important at 80 to 100 km over England. The most striking thing is how large the changes are. When the wind changes from 20 m/sec toward the north to 20 m/sec toward the south, this is a tidal change of 40 m/sec or about 80 knots. At the earth's surface, this would be the same as the wind starting from zero and increasing to hurricane speed. The prediction of the dynamo theory that the tidal winds at 80 to 100 km must be very strong is certainly borne out by these measurements.

Although at Jodrell Bank the semi-diurnal tide, with the winds changing direction every 6 hours, seems to be more important than the diurnal tide, a word of caution is in order. The Jodrell Bank equipment was unable to measure the exact height of a meteor trail, and the results were based on meteor trails at all altitudes between 80 and 105 km. At Adelaide in Australia, where such height determinations can be made, the diurnal tide seems to be at least as important at any one level. However, the diurnal tidal winds at Adelaide change direction rapidly as the altitude changes. The same may also be true at Jodrell Bank, so that the diurnal tide, although large at any one altitude, does not show up when measurements from all altitudes between 80 and 105 km are lumped together.

Much more work, both observational and theoretical, needs to be done before the atmospheric tides are completely understood. Their great importance in the upper atmosphere and their effects on the magnetic field and on the ionosphere are causing many scientists to study them now.

With many problems, scientists sometimes think of the upper atmosphere and the lower atmosphere as being quite separate. But in the case of the tides it is clear that the whole atmosphere is involved and, for once, meteorologists, aeronomers, radio engineers, and geomagneticians can join together and work on a problem of common interest.

VIII

Light from the Upper Atmosphere— the Aurora and the Airglow

The aurora and the airglow differ from each other in many ways, but they have one important characteristic in common. Both are radiation that actually originates in the earth's upper atmosphere (that is, is radiated by atoms and molecules in the upper atmosphere). This radiation can be detected at the earth's surface, either by eye or by means of sensitive instruments, and studied. Such studies can be used to deduce a great deal of information about the upper atmosphere, for instance the kinds of atoms and molecules that are present there.

Notice that we have said that the light in the aurora and airglow comes from the *upper* atmosphere. Molecules in the lower atmosphere give off radiation in the infrared part of the spectrum, at wavelengths greater than about 5 microns (see Table 1), but such radiation is not included under the terms "aurora" and "airglow." The radiation that is included is in the ultra-violet, visible, and near infrared wavelengths.

The energy that is radiated in the aurora and airglow comes originally from different sources, which is one reason for distinguishing between the two. The energy for the aurora comes from charged particles, mostly electrons and protons that come from the sun and enter the upper atmosphere at very high velocities. As these particles collide with the ordinary air molecules, their kinetic energy (energy of motion) is changed to other forms of energy in a very complicated series of chemical reactions. Some of the kinetic energy is eventually converted to the radiated energy that we see as the aurora. On the other hand, energy for the airglow comes initially from the sun's electromagnetic radiation, some of which is absorbed by atoms and molecules in the upper atmosphere. Again after a complicated series of chemical reactions, some of this is converted to the radiated energy that we call the airglow. There are many things that we do not know about the details of the chemical reactions leading from high-velocity particles to aurora, or from solar radiation to airglow. On the other hand, there are many things that we do know; but a meaningful discussion of these could easily fill a book of this size all by itself. So we must resist the temptation to go into further detail.

The most obvious reasons for distinguishing between aurora and airglow are their patterns of occurrence and the enormous difference in their brightness. The airglow is present at all times and places, but it is so faint that it can be detected only with the aid of sensitive instruments. The aurora is quite common in high latitudes, but only rarely seen in middle and low latitudes, as we shall discuss in more detail later in this chapter. But an auroral display when it does occur is easily visible to the naked eye and often presents a vivid, striking panorama of changing colors and forms.

Some Characteristics of the Aurora

An auroral display sometimes lasts for only a few minutes, but it may persist for several hours. Its apparent brightness in the sky occasionally equals that of the full moon, and a bright aurora may cast enough light on the ground so that one can read a newspaper. The patterns of light take on many forms, shapes, and colors, all of which may change rapidly or gradually during the duration of the phenomenon. As a matter of fact, there is an international classification system for auroral forms, some of which are illustrated in Plates V–VIII, but we shall not describe this system in detail.

Considering its easy visibility and striking appearance, you should not be surprised to learn that the aurora was well known to the ancient Greeks and Romans. Seneca described it as follows:

"Sometimes flames are seen in the sky, either stationary or full of movement. Several kinds are known: the abysses, when beneath a luminous crown the heavenly fire is wanting, forming as it were the circular entrance to a cavern; the turns (*pithitae*), when a great rounded flame in the form of a barrel is seen to move from place to place, or to burn immovable; the gulfs (*chasmata*), when the heaven seems to open and to vomit flames which before were hidden in its depths. These fires present the most varied colours: some are a vivid red; others resemble a faint and dying flame; some are white; others scintillate; others finally are of an even yellow, and emit neither rays nor projections. Among these phenomena should be ranged those appearances as of the heavens on fire so often reported by historians; sometimes these fires are high enough to shine among the stars; at others, so low that they might be taken for the reflection of a distant burning homestead or city. This is what happened under Tiberius, when the cohorts hurried to the succour of the colony of Ostia, believing it to be on fire. During the greater part of the night the heaven appeared to be illuminated by a faint light resembling a thick smoke."

A thirteenth-century Norseman speculated on the cause of the aurora as follows:

"Some people maintain that this light is a reflection of the fire which surrounds the seas of the north and of the south; others say that it is the reflection of the sun when it is below the horizon; for my part I think that it is produced by the ice which radiates at night the light which it has absorbed by day."

These speculations were not correct, but they show remarkable curiosity and ingenuity. This man might well have become a successful scientist if born six or seven centuries later.

By the late nineteenth century, it was well known that the aurora is much more frequently seen in some locations than in others. In 1881, a German scientist, H. Fritz, used his voluminous collection of auroral reports to demonstrate the main features of the geographical distribution. These features are illustrated in Figure 29, taken from a more recent compilation (1944) by Dr. Harry Vestine. The heavy curves in

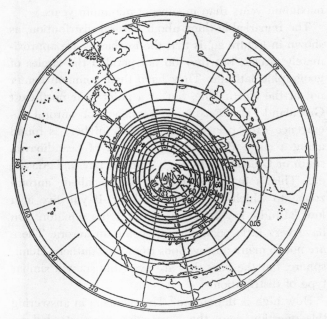

Figure 29. Auroral Frequency in the Northern Hemisphere. The "isochasms" tell the percentage of clear nights on which, on the average, the aurora will be seen. Notice that the lines are not centered at the geographical North Pole.

Figure 29 are called "isochasms," and they are labeled according to the percentage of nights when aurora would be visible in the absence of cloudiness. For example, everywhere along the curve labeled "5.0," which passes near Boston, Massachusetts, aurora would be visible on 5 per cent of the nights if there were never any clouds to obscure it. (Actually this is an average taken over many years. As we shall see later, the chances for an aurora are better in sunspot-maximum years than in sunspot-minimum years.)

The remarkable thing about auroral distribution, as shown in Figure 29, is that the isochasms are approximately circles, but they do not parallel the circles of geographic latitude. They have their common center not at the North Pole, but at a point near northwest Greenland. The maximum frequency of auroral occurrence (100 per cent of the clear nights) is found along a curve that passes just north of Scandinavia, south of Greenland, through Hudson Bay and Alaska, etc. This is in the middle of the so-called "auroral zone," to which we shall refer later. If you live at a low latitude, say between 30° and the equator, you have very little possibility of seeing an aurora. There are not so many observations from the Southern Hemisphere, but the ones that are available show a similar type of distribution.

How high is the aurora? The pioneers in answering this question were the Norwegian scientists, led by Carl Störmer, who devoted most of his life to a study of the aurora. The method that they developed is illustrated in Figure 30. Two observers, situated at least 25 km apart and in contact with each other by telephone, photograph the same portion of the sky at

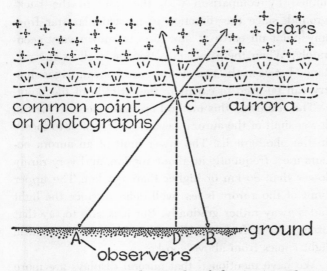

stars

common point on photographs

C

aurora

A D B ground

observers

Figure 30. Measuring the Height of the Aurora. This is the method developed by the Norwegians. The two observers (A and B) are at least 25 km apart. They locate a common point (C) on their simultaneous photographs. By comparison with the stars in the background, the direction of C from both A and B is determined. Since the distance from A to B is already known, trigonometry may be used to determine the lengths of AC and BC, and ultimately that of CD, which is the height of the aurora.

the same time. When the photographs are compared later, a particular point on the aurora, one where there is some distinguishing feature of form or shape or brightness, is located on both photographs. The direction of this point from each of the stations is determined by comparison with the stars in the background, since the direction of a particular star from any point on earth at any time is known very accurately. When these two directions as well as the distance between the two stations are known, trigonometry can be used to calculate the altitude of the point.

The results of this method are most definite for the lower limit of the aurora, because it is easiest to locate in the photographs. The lower limit of an aurora occurs most frequently at about 105 km, and very rarely lower than 80 km or higher than 150 km. The upper limit of the aurora is less well defined, since the light fades away rather gradually. But it is safe to say that except for a few special types of aurora very little light comes from above 200 km.

We have mentioned that auroral displays are more frequent during sunspot-maximum years than during sunspot-minimum years. This refers to the large and bright aurorae of the type that are visible from middle latitudes. There is other evidence that such aurorae are connected directly with a high level of solar activity. In Chapter 4, we spoke of the occurrence of solar flares in certain active regions on the sun. In Chapter 6, we pointed out some of the direct and immediate effects of solar flares on the ionosphere, notably in the production of greatly increased numbers of ions and electrons in the D region. To continue with the description of this chain of events, we should now mention that a large auroral display usually follows a pronounced solar flare and the resulting ionosphere effects by about 24 hours. However, not all sunspot groups have active regions that produce flares, and not all flares produce aurora. So the connection between aurora and sunspots is a general, statistical one; that is, it does not necessarily hold for an individual sunspot.

The Auroral Spectrum

Light from the aurora can be passed through a spectrograph and the wavelength of the light emitted in lines can be determined, as was discussed in Chapter 2 in connection with observational methods. As we also discussed there, a particular line at a particular wavelength can be identified as coming from a certain kind of atom or molecule.

The auroral spectrum has a very large number of lines, and it has been studied extensively. These studies show that the light is coming from molecular nitrogen, ionized molecular nitrogen (that is, N_2 with one of its electrons missing), molecular oxygen, atomic nitrogen, ionized atomic nitrogen, atomic oxygen, and ionized atomic oxygen. Two of the strongest lines are emitted by atomic oxygen; these also show up in the airglow and we shall discuss them in more detail in that connection.

An interesting conclusion is that some of these lines can be radiated only if the atoms and molecules have been exposed to a large amount of energy. To put it another way, ordinary electromagnetic energy from the sun cannot be expected to affect the upper-atmosphere atoms and molecules in such a way that they can radiate these lines. This is just one of the arguments for the theory that high-energy particles from the sun are responsible for the aurora.

Some Explanations of Auroral Features—
The Earth's Magnetic Field

In outlining some of the auroral characteristics, we mentioned some rather peculiar facts, without giving any explanation for them. Why does the geographical distribution of aurorae have the features shown in Figure 29? Why do great auroral displays follow solar flares by about 24 hours instead of occurring immediately afterward?

These things can be explained if we assume that the aurora is caused by charged particles rather than by ordinary electromagnetic radiation. But first, we must discuss briefly the earth's magnetic field and its effect on charged particles.

The earth's main magnetic field (the geomagnetic field) arises from causes inside the earth, but its influence extends to the outermost part of the atmosphere. It can be described by "lines of force," or lines that show the direction of the force acting on a magnet. Some of these lines of force are shown in Figure 31. Notice carefully that the "top" of this figure, where the line of force is perpendicular to the earth's surface, is *not* the ordinary North Pole. It is a point in Greenland, near its northwest coast, which is called the geomagnetic North Pole. If you study the direction of the lines of force in Figure 31, you can see why a compass needle does not point exactly toward the geographic north. On the average, over the entire earth, the needle turns so that its north-seeking end points toward the geomagnetic North Pole in northwest Greenland.[8] Notice also that the needle, if it were allowed to swing in the vertical, would point somewhat downward (in the Northern Hemisphere), the more so the closer it is to the geomagnetic North Pole.

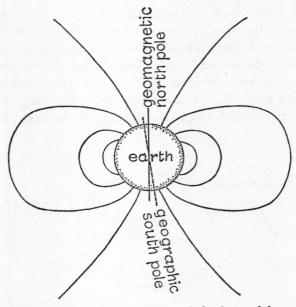

Figure 31. Lines of Force. Some of the lines of force in the earth's magnetic field are shown here. Note the difference in position between the geographic and geomagnetic poles.

[8] At a particular location, the direction may be somewhat different from this. For example, at Boston, Massachusetts, a compass needle points 15° west of geographic north, which is toward a point somewhat west of the geomagnetic North Pole. Maps showing the exact direction at all locations are prepared and kept up to date by the U. S. Navy Oceanographic Office.

A charged particle, such as an electron, moving in
a magnetic field, such as the earth's, is subject to a
force which depends on the direction and strength of
the magnetic field and on the direction and speed of
the particle's motion. The net result of this force is
that a charged particle coming from the sun usually
follows a complicated spiraling path around and along
one of the lines of force as it approaches the earth.
The usual charged particles with just average energy
are caught up and forced to follow a line of force that
extends quite far from the earth and comes back to
earth fairly near (but not right at) the geomagnetic
North or South Poles (see Figure 32). As these par-

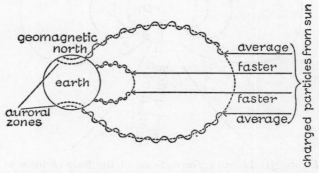

Figure 32. The Paths of Charged Particles in the Earth's
    Magnetic Field. Most particles follow a spiral-
    ing path centered on one of the outside lines of
    force and therefore enter the atmosphere at
    high latitudes. These cause the "auroral zones"
    (at about 60° to 70° geomagnetic latitude). A
    few of the more rapid particles are caught by
    lines closer to the earth and therefore spiral in
    at lower latitudes.

ticles enter the upper atmosphere, they cause the aurora in these regions, which are called the *auroral zones*. The regions of maximum aurora, as you saw in Figure 29, are about 20° to 30° from the geomagnetic poles. On the other hand, at a time of solar disturbance, and especially after a solar flare, the charged particles approach the earth with greater speed and are able to get closer to the earth before they begin to follow a line of force. The lines of force that are closer to the earth come back to the earth's surface in lower latitudes, and particles entering along these lines of force can cause aurora in the lower latitudes.

As for the delay between a solar flare and a great auroral display, this is simply due to the time required for the charged particles to travel the distance from the sun to the earth. Electromagnetic radiation, moving with the "speed of light," can cover the distance between sun and earth in about 8 minutes. The charged particles are much slower, although still very fast by our usual standards. Leaving the sun at the same time as the electromagnetic radiation, they arrive here about 24 hours later.

Some Characteristics of the Airglow

The airglow, which we discussed briefly in Chapter 1, is much less spectacular than the aurora and less well known, but its study has paid rich dividends in adding to our knowledge of the upper atmosphere.

Over 100 years ago it was known that the faint light of the night sky, when studied with a spectrograph, contained a line at a wavelength of 5577 A. This line had been observed in the auroral spectrum, and its presence even in the absence of aurora indicated that the upper atmosphere gives off at least a faint glow at all times. In the early 1900s it was even called "permanent aurora" or "nonpolar aurora." This, along with other emissions, is what we now call the "airglow."

The line at 5577 A is called the "green line," because light of that wavelength appears green to the human eye (this line and the "red line" were mentioned in Chapter 2). For many years the kind of atom or molecule which radiated the green line was unknown. This wavelength was not observed in the laboratory until 1925, when it was finally produced by passing an electrical discharge through a mixture of oxygen and helium. After a few years of further experiment and theory, it was clearly established that the green line comes from atomic oxygen. This was the first clear-cut evidence for the presence of atomic oxygen in the upper atmosphere, and it aroused a great deal of interest among scientists.

This is not the only example of information about the composition of the upper atmosphere gained from studies of the airglow. In Chapter 5, we mentioned the presence of hydroxyl, OH, and its importance in the airglow. Another, and even more curious, example is sodium (Na). Two prominent lines of sodium at 5890 A and 5896 A are easily detected; but nobody knows just why there should be any sodium in the upper atmosphere, or where it comes from. Two competing theories are that sea salt (NaCl) is carried up to the upper atmosphere where it is broken up by sunlight into atoms of Na and of Cl (chlorine); or that the sodium comes from the vaporization of meteors.

Not much sodium needs to be there to explain the observations.

There is another prominent line in the airglow from atomic oxygen, the "red line" at 6332 A. There are also many lines from O_2. However, there is not much radiation from nitrogen, either molecular or atomic.

There has been much difficulty in determining the altitude from which the airglow comes. The standard method used for aurorae, described earlier in this chapter, does not work very well because the airglow is so faint and also because it has so few identifiable features. The best method uses a rocket which carries up an instrument that measures the intensity of a particular airglow feature, such as the green line. With the instrument pointing upward, the airglow is detected while the rocket is below the emitting layer, but not after the rocket has passed up through it. These measurements have shown that most of the airglow emission comes from the lower thermosphere, at around 100 km. The hydroxyl and sodium lines come at least partially from the mesosphere. The red line of atomic oxygen comes from a much greater elevation, at least above 150 km.

Although the airglow and aurora are no longer mysterious, we certainly do not have a perfect understanding of them. Much has been learned, but much remains to be learned in the future. But let us turn next to the outer fringe—the "edge" of the atmosphere.

IX

The Outermost Atmosphere

The earth's outermost atmosphere, the part above a few hundred kilometers, is a region of extremely low density. Near sea level, the number of atoms and molecules in a cubic centimeter of air is about 2×10^{19}; near 600 km it is only about 2×10^{7}, which is the sea-level value divided by a million million. At sea level, an atom or molecule can be expected, on the average, to move about 7×10^{-6} cm before colliding with another particle; at the 600-km level this distance, called the "mean free path," is about 10 km. Near sea level, an atom or molecule, on the average, undergoes about 7×10^{9} such collisions each second; near 600 km, this number is reduced to about 1 each minute.

In this near vacuum, where the atmosphere fades away and blends into interplanetary space, there are new and different problems for the atmospheric scientist. We are just beginning to understand what some of these problems are, and we are far from a satisfactory solution to most of them. This chapter will introduce the reader to some of these problems.

In discussing the outer atmosphere, we sometimes use the word "exosphere" and sometimes the word "magnetosphere." The word "exosphere" was coined by Dr. Lyman Spitzer in 1949, from the Greek "exo" meaning "outside." It is usually used when the behavior of neutral particles, carrying no electric charge, is being studied. "Magnetosphere" refers to more or less the same altitude limits, but is the preferred term when the properties of the earth's magnetic field and its effect on charged particles are important to the discussion.

The Exosphere

The atoms or molecules of a gas are always in rapid motion, moving faster, on the average, when the temperature is higher. Ordinarily, a particular atom or molecule can be expected to collide with another very, very often with a resultant change in its direction of motion. In the exosphere, collisions are so infrequent that they have no important effects on the motion of neutral particles. However, just below the exosphere, in the upper thermosphere, collisions are still frequent enough to be important. Nevertheless, a certain fraction of the upward-moving particles will escape this region without suffering any collision and move up into the exosphere. There, an individual particle is "on its own." Most of these will fall back to the lower denser regions under the influence of gravity, just as a rocket falls back to earth after reaching the top of its trajectory. Some faster-moving particles may go into orbit and circle the earth, like artificial satellites. Particles with enough initial energy, that is, those which left the base of the exosphere with a high enough velocity, may even escape the earth's gravitational field altogether and move out into space.

Of course, there is no absolutely sharp dividing line between a region where collisions are "important" and one where they are "unimportant." As the likelihood of collisions becomes smaller and smaller, the thermosphere blends into the exosphere. The dividing line is usually taken to be at about 500 km, from which level a certain fraction of the neutral atoms and molecules are able to escape upward into the exosphere.

Temperature and Composition of the Exosphere

Before asking what the temperature of the exosphere is, we should first ask what is meant by "temperature," in this nearly empty region at the edge of space. When collisions are frequent, the temperature of a gas is a measure of the average speed of the molecules or atoms in their random motion. In the exosphere, there is no appreciable number of collisions, but remember that the particles there have come recently from a lower, denser region below the exosphere. It turns out that for many purposes we can think of the exosphere as having the same temperature as that lower region. For example, we can compute particle velocities, in the sense of an average, and use the hydrostatic equation, at least up to a few thousand kilometers, if we assume that the temperature is the same at all levels in the exosphere as it is at the bottom of the exosphere.

The thermosphere, just below the exosphere, shows wide temperature variations from time to time, as was discussed in Chapter 3. According to the arguments given above, these wide variations apply to the exosphere as well. Thus the thermosphere and exosphere are much hotter by day than by night, and at sunspot-maximum than at sunspot-minimum. As pointed out in Chapter 3, the temperature may vary from 700°C to 2000°C. This represents the average speed of the molecules, and is not to say that if you were there you would feel that hot.

As discussed in Chapter 5, the composition of the thermosphere is greatly affected by diffusive equilibrium, in which the lighter gases predominate at higher levels. In the upper part of the thermosphere, above 200 to 300 km, atomic oxygen already predominates over the heavier molecular nitrogen. In the exosphere, this trend continues. At high enough levels the atmosphere is composed mostly of helium, and at still higher levels of atomic hydrogen, the lightest gas of all.

Figure 33 shows the results of some computations made in Belgium by G. Kockarts and Marcel Nicolet. When the thermosphere and exosphere are comparatively cold, helium becomes the most abundant atom at about 600 km and hydrogen at about 1000 km. When the thermosphere is hot, as during the day near sunspot-maximum, the atmosphere expands and the gases spread out over a greater vertical distance. Then, helium predominates between about 1300 km and 5000 km, hydrogen above 5000 km. Incidentally, the presence of the helium and hydrogen layers in the exosphere is not simply a matter of theory or calculation. They have been directly detected and measured from satellites. The presence of neutral helium was first detected by a mass spectrometer on the Explorer XVII satellite in 1963.

Atmospheric Escape

As pointed out earlier, an atom or molecule leaving the thermosphere and entering the exosphere may have acquired its escape velocity and leave the

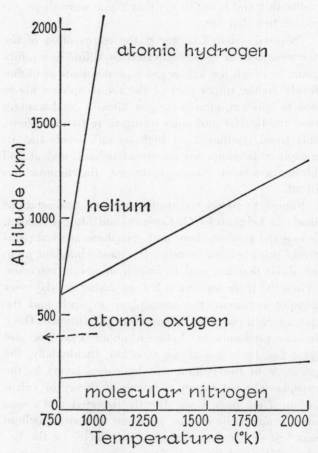

Figure 33. The Distribution of Most Prevalent Gases in
the Outermost Atmosphere. Each line shows
the temperatures and altitudes for which the
two gases above and below it are present in
equal quantity.

earth's gravitational field. Such an atom or molecule is lost to the atmosphere forever. If this happened often enough, we would eventually have no atmosphere left. This process is called "atmospheric escape."

Whether atmospheric escape is fast enough seriously to deplete the atmosphere of the earth, or of any planet, depends on three things. It depends first of all on the mass of the planet, the heavier planets having a stronger gravitational attraction. The second factor is the temperature at the base of the exosphere; if the temperature is higher a larger fraction of the atoms will have a high enough velocity to escape. Thirdly, for any one planet and a particular temperature, the lighter atoms, such as hydrogen and helium, can escape the most rapidly.

The smaller planets and natural satellites, such as Mercury and our moon, could not be expected to have retained an atmosphere over long time periods, if they ever had one at all. Mars, with a gravitational attraction about one-third that of the earth's is a borderline case, where the importance of atmospheric escape depends on the temperature of the Martian exosphere. Since we now know from observations that Mars has very little atmosphere, we can infer that atmospheric escape must have played an important role. On the other hand, the massive planets like Jupiter and Saturn can hold in even the lightest of gases, hydrogen and helium.

But what about our own atmosphere? Considering the earth's gravitational attraction and the observed exospheric temperatures, the calculations are reassuring. Only hydrogen can escape at a rapid enough rate to affect its atmospheric abundance seriously. Helium can be expected to escape very, very slowly and the heavier gases hardly at all. Our atmosphere is going to be with us for a long, long time.

The Magnetosphere and the Solar Wind

All of the discussion so far in this chapter applies to neutral particles. Charged particles, ions and electrons, behave very differently, because their motions are affected by the earth's magnetic field. At low elevations, say below about 200 km, the charged particles are still forced to move more or less with the neutral particles, because of collisions (although even here, they have important differential motions, as noted in the dynamo theory). Above about 200 km, the charged particles move more or less independently of the neutral particles. This part of the atmosphere is called the "magnetosphere" and its outer boundary occurs where the magnetic field caused by the earth becomes less important than the magnetic fields due to charged particles moving through interplanetary space.

The present estimates of the size and shape of the magnetosphere are shown in Figure 34. On the side of the earth facing the sun, it extends outward for about 10 earth radii, or 57,000 km. The earth's radius is 6370 km. Ten earth radii are 63,700 km measured from the center of the earth or about 57,000 km measured from the earth's surface. On the side away from the sun, there is a much more extended region called a "tail," which may reach out for hundreds of earth radii, or well beyond the moon, although this question is not yet settled.

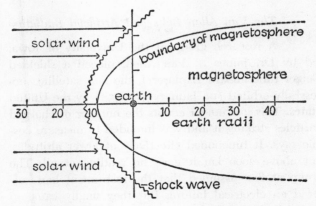

Figure 34. The Magnetosphere. Beyond about 30 earth radii, on the side of the earth away from the sun, there is some question about the extent of the magnetosphere. This uncertain region is denoted by the dotted lines.

The shape of the magnetosphere is a result of what is called the solar wind (or solar plasma). This is an onrushing stream, made up mostly of protons and electrons, which is continuously emitted by the sun. Its tremendous energy compresses the magnetosphere on the earth's sunward side. The degree of compression depends on the amount of solar activity. When solar activity is at its greatest, and the solar wind is strongest, the outer boundary of the magnetosphere may be forced to a position only 40,000 km above the earth.

Our understanding of the magnetosphere is very limited because only the far-ranging space probes can study it. A vast amount of work remains to be done.

The Van Allen Belts and Artificial Radiation

A research group at the University of Iowa, led by Dr. James A. Van Allen, placed a shielded Geiger tube aboard Explorer I, the first satellite successfully orbited (on January 31, 1958) by the United States. This instrument counts the number of charged particles striking it and was intended to measure cosmic rays. It functioned effectively at lower altitudes, but above 2000 km it gave no reading at all. The group at first assumed that the instrument had suffered an electrical failure. But they finally came to the realization, which was confirmed by later experiments, that it had been jammed by an unexpectedly high intensity of radiation.

This was the first evidence of what are now called the "Van Allen belts." Here energetic protons and electrons are trapped by the earth's magnetic field. They spiral back and forth, more or less from north to south and back again, along the lines of force of the earth's magnetic field (as shown in Figure 32).

There are two "doughnut-shaped" belts within the "Van Allen region," as shown in Figure 35. The inner belt is centered at about 1.5 earth radii (about 3200 km above the earth's surface), while the outer one is centered at about 3.5 earth radii. The high-energy particles in the inner belt are protons, those in the outer belt are electrons. We still do not know where these high-energy charged particles come from, whether from the lower atmosphere or from the sun, nor do we know how they gain their high energies.

When first discovered, the Van Allen belts seemed a serious threat to space travel, because of the lethal

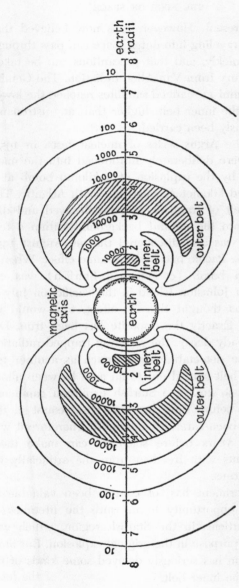

Figure 35. The Van Allen Region. The curves are contours of constant radiation intensity, measured in counts per second.

radiation present. However, it is now believed that astronauts traveling into outer space can pass through the belts quickly, and that precautions can be taken to avoid injury from Van Allen radiation. The Gemini 10 and Gemini 11 manned satellites reached the lower portion of the inner belt, higher than any astronauts had previously been carried.

During the Argus series of nuclear tests, in 1959, electrons were deliberately introduced into the magnetosphere by the explosion of a kiloton bomb at a few hundred kilometers, over the South Atlantic. The resulting belt of trapped electrons decayed and disappeared into the natural background within a few months. It was also discovered that an August 1958 test over the Pacific had had the same effect. When a 1.4-megaton bomb (code-named Starfish) was exploded over Johnston Island in the Pacific, on July 9, 1962, it was thought that its effect, too, would be short-lived. Exactly the opposite has been true. Despite its steady decay, the resulting trapped radiation may still be detectable for as much as another ten years. The belt spread out to an area between about 300 and 5000 km. The Starfish explosion came unfortunately before the natural electron count in the region had been carefully measured. Therefore it will be several years before scientists can make these measurements with freedom from the artificially injected electrons.

The experiment has, of course, been valuable in giving the opportunity to measure the lifetimes of trapped particles in the Starfish region, which was part of the purpose in the original explosion. But Starfish radiation has seriously delayed some kinds of research on the inner belt.

X

The Challenge
of the Upper Atmosphere

In the preceding chapters, we have discussed some of the problems of the upper atmosphere and some of the past and present attempts to solve them. Although most of the important problems have been considered, it has not been possible in the space available to include most of the details, or even to touch on a few other interesting phenomena like mother-of-pearl clouds, noctilucent clouds, and cosmic rays. Now in this last chapter let us try to look briefly into the future of upper-atmospheric research. Of course, while doing this, we must realize that the future will probably hold many surprises, which are not foreseeable at present.

General Interest and Practical Applications

There seems to be no question that the upper atmosphere will assume more and more practical importance in the activities of mankind as time goes on.

Consider, for example, commercial air travel. Once confined to the lowest few kilometers of the atmosphere, it now ranges throughout the troposphere, as today's commercial jets routinely fly at or near tropopause level. The supersonic aircraft necessary to accomplish air travel in the lower stratosphere, say at around 20 km, are now in an advanced stage of design, and such travel is only a few years away. The sophisticated air traveler a few years from now will hear about ozone, stratospheric warmings, and the stratospheric summer-winter wind reversal, much as he today hears about the jet stream and clear-air turbulence of the upper troposphere. An eventual advance to still higher altitudes seems inevitable, although its timing is impossible to predict in detail. Is it too farfetched to expect that some day a rocket ship will transport passengers halfway around the world in less than an hour?

But air travel is only one example of a growing list of important problems involving the upper atmosphere. The military will maintain a keen interest in the medium through which some of the advanced weapons systems must travel. Satellites circling the earth will perform an ever-increasing list of tasks, such as weather observing, long-distance communication, and mapping of the earth's surface. The ionosphere, and its effect on radio communication, can only grow in practical importance. And, of course, as mentioned near the beginning of this book, exploration of space necessarily requires traversals of the upper atmosphere by manned and unmanned vehicles.

All of this can only mean a rapidly accelerating rate of observation and research on the properties of the upper atmosphere. The advances of the past twenty years, as impressive as they now seem, are only a small beginning.

Can we foresee some of the problems that will have to be solved? Throughout this book, we have tried to call attention to many specific scientific problems that remain unsolved, but there is really not much point in trying to repeat these and compile a "list." Anyway, the list would probably change drastically in the next few years as these problems are solved and replaced by new ones. We can, however, call attention to certain developments in observations and research that will certainly have to take place.

Observing Systems

We now possess the technology and the know-how to measure almost everything that we think we need to measure in the upper atmosphere. Of course, in some instances, present-day techniques are crude and not sufficiently accurate, so they require considerable refinement. However, the real difficulty is that most upper-atmospheric measurements are very expensive and, as a consequence, are carried out all too infrequently. What we shall have to develop, at least in some cases, are simpler and more economical observing systems that will allow frequent observations at a large number of places.

In some instances, this goal may be achieved through ground-based observations. Such observations are usually inexpensive, because even an expensive item of fixed equipment may be used long enough to make the cost per observation low. Another promising possibility is indirect measurements from a satellite of the atmosphere below it. For example, much thought has been given to deducing the temperature and ozone distributions in the upper stratosphere from radiation emitted by the upper stratosphere and detected by a satellite orbiting at a much higher level. Although the initial cost of orbiting a satellite is large, it can stay up for many months and observe frequently over wide areas of the earth, including areas that are impractical for surface observations.

The trouble with both ground-based and satellite observations of this type is that they are often not sufficiently accurate. This is not so much a matter of technology and instrumentation, as it is an inherent difficulty of "measuring from a distance." To put it a little more technically, the information content of the signals sent by the atmosphere to the ground or to a satellite is limited. In many cases there is just no substitute for carrying an instrument, by balloon, rocket, or satellite, into that part of the atmosphere where the measurement must be made.

We have the vehicles and instruments to do this. Balloons have a maximum useful altitude, which has nearly been reached. Satellites have a minimum useful altitude if they are to stay aloft for any length of time. The intermediate atmosphere, say from 40 to 200 km, can be reached by rockets. However, the frequent use of rockets poses a serious safety problem, and a formidable cost problem. Rockets cannot be fired up through the air lanes without rigid controls, and they cannot be allowed to return to earth in inhabited areas. Proper scheduling can eliminate danger to air travel and foolproof self-destruction devices can prevent the rocket's return to earth, but both require much more development and will aggravate the cost problem. In the final analysis, that is the vital factor. However, as the cost of rockets decreases and the need for observations increases, as both inevitably will, the time will come when man will seriously consider routine and frequent rocket observations of the upper atmosphere just as he has now established routine and frequent balloon observations of the lower atmosphere.

Trends in Research

There are certain obvious trends in upper-atmospheric research that are related to our society's growing need for and support of research and to our rapidly advancing technology. Thus, it seems safe to predict that more money will be spent, more people will be trained, more and better observations will be made, and more sophisticated computers will be used to analyze these observations. These generalities are applicable in varying degrees to all types of research. In addition, there are problems peculiar to upper-atmospheric studies that have to be worked out within this framework of increased activity.

An important one is the development of upper-atmospheric research, or aeronomy, as a unified field of study. Perhaps you have already noticed that different problems connected with the upper atmosphere require different kinds of specialized knowledge. Thus, certain aspects of astronomy, chemistry, physics, meteorology, and engineering all enter at different places. In the past, most scientists interested in the upper atmosphere have had their primary training and interest in only one of these fields and have been drawn, sometimes almost by accident, into applications of their knowledge to some problem of the upper atmosphere. As a result, there was often too little communication among the different scientists and too little appreciation for the problems of the upper atmosphere as a whole. This is changing now, through the organization of conferences, the production of reference and textbooks, and the development of centers of study and research devoted to the interrelated problems of the upper atmosphere. This trend will surely continue.

Another important factor in upper-atmospheric research is the recognition and study of the upper atmosphere as a dynamic, moving, changing medium. Until the International Geophysical Year, July 1957– December 1958, it was common to think of an observation at one place or at one time as being representative of the phenomenon observed at all places and all times. Partly, this was a matter of necessity because of the scarcity of observations. To some extent though, it apparently reflected a lack of appreciation for the variability of the atmosphere. For example, the old question "What is the mean molecular weight at 150 km?" might now be phrased "What is the mean molecular weight at 150 km and how much does it change with latitude, season, and phase of the sunspot cycle?"—or even, "Does it change from one day to the next?" It is also clear that many things cannot be explained in terms of an equilibrium in a static medium. The atmosphere itself moves and transports heat, momentum, and various gases from one place to another.

Altogether, the future is exciting for research on the upper atmosphere. The demands are growing, the problems are challenging, and the results are deeply rewarding. If you are a young man or woman contemplating a scientific career, you might like to consider the upper atmosphere.

Index

Date Due